Personal Trainers' Guide to Earning Top Dollar

A Cutting-Edge Guide to Maximizing Your Income as a Personal Trainer

Ben Greenfield

ISBN: 978-1-60679-068-7
Library of Congress Control Number: 2009933131
Cover design: Studio J Art & Design
Book layout: Studio J Art & Design
Front cover images: ©2009 Jupiterimages Corporation

Healthy Learning
P.O. Box 1828
Monterey, CA 93942
www.healthylearning.com

Dedication

*This book is dedicated to giving America
a healthier body, mind, and economy.*

Contents

Preface

As a fitness and nutrition professional, you are drastically underpaid. While it really is true that you can make six to seven figures as a personal trainer, the traditional industry is not set up to accommodate the large salary that you could (and should) be making. Instead, you're stuck with a small salary or an hourly pay structure. However, to truly succeed in the fitness business, you must take matters into your own hands, and the only way to accomplish this success is if you have multiple income streams. I've written this book to identify those streams and provide you with the exact instructions for easily commanding your income and creating your fitness empire in each of the following markets:

- Face-to-face personal training
- Physician referral systems
- Online training
- Web 2.0 technology marketing
- Outsourcing to local and overseas merchants
- Dietary supplement industry
- Nutritional consulting
- Book, audio, and DVD sales
- Corporate and home training
- Public appearances and marketing

Each chapter in this book makes learning how to *train for top dollar* as convenient as possible, by providing you with the necessary step-by-step instructions, forms, templates, phone numbers, websites, real life examples, and insider tips and tricks. Are you tired of showing up to your routine personal training job each day to train a handful of clients and receive an hourly session fee? Do you have a personal training studio that struggles each month to meet the bottom line? Are you ready to command an exorbitant salary as a respected fitness or nutrition expert? Whether you are a health club owner, private studio trainer, student personal trainer, or gym employee, *Personal Trainers' Guide to Earning Top Dollar* will teach you everything you need to know, straight from the mind of Ben Greenfield, the nation's top personal training business expert.

Introduction

I clearly remember my first personal training session. As a young college sophomore in 2000, I was pursuing an exercise-science degree from University of Idaho and had successfully landed a side job as a personal trainer at the downtown gym. This time was my time to shine. The months of studying for the National Strength and Conditioning Association certification, the exercise physiology classes, the new cotton t-shirt with the bold word "TRAINER" on the back all led to this moment.

The prospective client's name was Bill. My first question was awkward and forced, "So Bill, what would you say your, um, goals for working out...are?" Of course, over the past eight years I've discovered dozens of magical key phrases, conversations, and questions that I could have presented to kick off this initial consultation, but back then I didn't know any of these methods. I was a stammering, nervous rookie who was probably more apprehensive about the ensuing conversation than the out-of-shape guy sitting across from me. He just shrugged, "I guess I just want to find out more about how to use some of the stuff in the gym, and not get hurt."

Red Flag! If only I had known better. As it turns out, the meeting with Bill, and the next dozen consultations with other gym-goers, would be a series of initial visits for new members eager to use their complementary personal training session for a guided free introduction to the gym. For the next several weeks, until I landed a paying "client," I would spend my valuable certification and education in exercise science as a type of tour guide, explaining the detailed intricacies of the machine chest press, while being careful to point out the clearly labeled exercise instructions and pictures on the side of the machine that informed the user exactly what I was telling them in the first place.

That experience was like being trapped on a hamster wheel—an endless series of repetitive sessions with people who just wanted a free handout. That gym, and most national health clubs today, operate with this very same structure. In Chapter 1, I reveal the exact blueprint of a much more effective and high paying business fee structure— a structure that doesn't cheapen the personal trainer or leave the client feeling like he is in a sales session.

After three months, and a small handful of clients who paid merely 20 to 25 dollars per one hour session, I realized that this career approach just wasn't working. Not only was I spending massive amounts of time fulfilling free consultations for new members (the gym compensated the trainers a measly "fit-time" wage for this activity, which is a common industry practice), but I was devoting hours of my own personal time to writing workouts, evaluating exercise-test results, and trying to figure out ways to drum up new business. And since the gym takes a large percentage of earnings, I was receiving after-tax earnings of 12 to 13 dollars per hour, which was really closer to seven to eight dollars per hour, once my personal time outside the session was taken into consideration. All that education and time, and I was making the wages of a pizza boy, without the tips.

However, I thought of myself as a bit of an outside-the-box entrepreneur, so when confronted with this time/income dilemma, I quickly discovered ways to maximize both time and income in my personal-training position. The philosophies and practices from an entire decade of experience, which I outline in this book, were in their infancy, but began their formation with my realization that the service performed by personal trainers is worth a very high salary – and a personal trainer can easily command a salary equal or greater than a physician, lawyer, or CEO.

Over the next three years of finishing my bachelor's degree and continuing to work as a personal trainer, I discovered a unique system called *speed templating* that allowed me to quickly create massive libraries of labeled workout routines to use for specific client profiles and demographics, designed the *cluster model* for multi-person training that immediately tripled my salary, taught myself how to use highly effective document design and marketing techniques (such as power headlining) for advertising inside and outside the gym, invented *cohort exercises* that ensured that my clients absolutely never dropped out of personal training, and immersed myself in specific speed reading and educational-material techniques, like the "one-read-rule" that allowed me to rapidly become a local recognized expert on fitness.

Using a few of the very same communication tools that I teach in *Personal Trainers' Guide to Earning Top Dollar* (specifically the squeaky wheel, good ol' boys method, and three list method), I scored undergraduate internships with Nike Sports Performance laboratories and the NFL, was named a top student researcher by the National Strength and Conditioning Association, and earned numerous awards and scholarships that nearly paid for my entire exercise-science education. But since books like *Personal Trainers' Guide to Earning Top Dollar* didn't exist, I spent massive amounts of my time and resources just figuring out how to use these techniques to maximize my time and resources. Looking back now, I had merely scratched the surface of my earning capabilities in these first few years as a rookie personal trainer.

After finishing my pre-med bachelor's degree and strength and conditioning certification, I turned down several medical school invitations and instead opted to stay at the University of Idaho and pursue a master's program in combined studies of advanced exercise physiology and biomechanics. As an active member of the university triathlon club, I was quickly rising to the status of "endurance expert," with a combined knowledge of physiology, biomechanics, and practical triathlon skills. In this role, I had discovered the wonderful world of niche marketing, and the exponential increase in business that can occur when the niche approach is combined with expert status. I call this one-two combo the *salary laser*, and in this book, you'll learn exactly how to use this tool to massively enhance your bottom line.

During my master's degree studies, I paid for my entire education with an internship as manager of the university wellness program. In this position, I suddenly had a massive university population at my fingertips, available to discover and practice brand new fee structure techniques, highly demographic-specific niche marketing methods, and successful self-promotion tools that left me inundated with eager baby-boomer triathletes looking for a coach, young sorority girls desperately looking to exercise physiology to lose those freshman 15, and college athletes anxious to discover how biomechanics could add a few miles an hour to their fastball. I was no more educated than my peers, but I had figured out the *special keys* that made individuals desperate for my services as a trainer.

As I worked toward finishing school, I used my *one-step-ahead model* to quickly host high-paying seminars and clinics that featured topics ranging the spectrum from children's fitness to personal training certification prep classes. I discovered how to have a booth-maximizing presence at health expos that caused people to literally wait in line 10 minutes for something as simple as a business card. I discovered how to use simple automated Internet information-collecting techniques to reduce my work and prep hours by half. By the time I completed my master's degree, that diminutive seven to eight dollars per hour had ballooned into 40 and 50 dollars per hour. In retrospect, 50 dollars per hour wasn't much, paling in comparison to the potential for earnings in the fitness industry. You must understand, these activities are not that difficult once the concepts are learned. In *Personal Trainers' Guide to Earning Top Dollar*, I share the methods that I used to achieve all this success, and much more.

After graduating in 2005 with a master's degree, I moved away from the fitness industry, and accepted a promising and high-paying job as a surgical sales consultant, which turned out to be one of the biggest mistakes of my life. I had fallen captive to one of the prevailing pitfall attitudes of the fitness industry—the idea that a personal trainer is merely a temporary pastime for young, struggling professionals attempting to move their way up in the world, much like a pool-boy, a burger-flipper, or a grocery-bagger. I failed to recognize the untapped wealth of a personal-training career, and spent an entire summer working in the knee and hip replacement medical industry before realizing the error of my ways.

Sure, the surgical sales paychecks were decent, but I spent hours observing operating-room procedures with my eyes, while my mind simultaneously wandered back to the fitness industry and the vast array of opportunities and ideas yet untouched. I went from complete control of my hours and income to being completely captive to the hours of the hospital and the medical-sales organization. On the bright side, I gained a wealth of knowledge about the health insurance protocols, the business of medicine, selling to physicians, and some backdoor operations of medical facilities that I later used as leverage to gain a steady stream of hundreds of high-paying clients. I will share these physician-networking secrets in Chapter 2.

After three months (three months too many), I quit surgical sales and immediately returned to the fitness industry, this time at a completely different gym in a completely different town. Although I had a customer base of zero clients, it took me only two weeks to completely fill my schedule with trainees from 8 am to 4 pm, and I immediately formed a client wait list. The methods of client networking, sales consultation closing, time management, and workout templating that I had taught myself as a young, struggling personal trainer in a small university town were actually working in a larger metropolitan environment. Amazing! I seamlessly transitioned to well over a thousand dollars per five day week.

Nonetheless, I was still subject to the fee structures, organizational models, and traditional, old-school personal-training program rules of a health club environment. Commissions, hourly salary limits, and competition from fellow trainers—the usual annoyances. I had to face it; the salary ceiling was solid. With the current model of health clubs and gyms, $60,000 to $80,000 per year was an unfortunate reality. Much better models existed, and I discovered them down the road. I share those models in this book.

It was time to strike out on my own. While continuing to work at the gym, I began to "moonlight" as an online-personal trainer and home-personal trainer. I purchased a laptop and self-taught myself domain purchasing, hosting set-up, FTP protocols, video uploading, photo optimization, HTML, Java, search engine submitting, form design, credit card processing, newsletters, mailing lists, and a host of other highly effective web techniques that I introduce to you in *Personal Trainers' Guide to Earning Top Dollar*. Of course, these techniques were rudimentary compared to the cutting-edge methods I learned over the ensuing four years of mastering my own web domains, but these initial steps were the necessary basics for developing an online-training model. At the same time, I also learned how to successfully run a home personal-training business, fulfilling legal, insurance, and tax obligations, while charging full personal training prices with zero overhead. In my unique model, my clients even paid for gas and driving expenses.

I made many mistakes while launching my online-training and home-training businesses. You don't need to do the same. In *Personal Trainers' Guide to Earning Top Dollar*, I teach you how to be up and running with a high dollar yielding online-personal training and home training presence in merely 24 hours, with an initial investment of under a hundred bucks.

Online training was tough to get off the ground and home training still wasn't quite enough. I hadn't yet learned the clandestine web-marketing techniques that I reveal in this book. I had to figure out another way to enhance my finances while I developed a more complete web presence, so I made another career-defining move.

Using high-speed writing and templating techniques borrowed from my personal-training marketing toolbox, I discovered self-publishing methods that allowed me to immediately design, print, and publish two separate book and DVD packages. With a combination of book and DVD sales via websites, local health clubs, and nutritional outlets, I was now making money while I slept! Imagine the satisfaction of finishing a personal-training session with a client and realizing you netted an extra 70 or 80 dollars in book sales during that single hour. Surprisingly, once I had waded through the dizzying host of self-publishing possibilities and weeded out the unproductive options, I found that this form of self-publishing is actually quite easy if you follow a simple set of rules that I outline in *Personal Trainers' Guide to Earning Top Dollar*. As a matter of fact, using the techniques that I outline, you can now publish your book and DVD for absolutely free, completely outsource book and DVD replication, order fulfillment, and shipping, and make a large royalty percentage every time your product is sold. Along the way, I refined the information product publishing to a simple model that I thoroughly explain in this book. I'll also teach you how to use book proposals, queries, agents, and editors if you decide to approach your publishing from a different angle.

Finally, after a year of simultaneous personal training, online training, and book/DVD publishing, I quit my job at the health club in order to expand my exploration of the limitless earning potential of the fitness industry. The next step was to set-up a private studio. But I took it one step further.

Using my physiology and biomechanics education, combined with simple marketing, networking, and design techniques, I joined forces with a prominent local physician and assisted with the launching of a sports-medicine facility that combined an expert team of physiologists, biomechanists, physical therapists, physicians, chiropractors, nutritionists, massage therapists, and personal trainers. Under one roof, we formed a beautifully networked business model that essentially featured a one-stop-shop for health, performance, injury treatment and prevention, fitness training, and nutrition management. Using this facility as a portal for my concurrent online business, I learned how to enhance my bottom line with membership fee structures, nutrition and supplement sales, public speaking and seminars, phone and e-mail consulting, press releases, magazine and newspaper networking, article contribution, and local media infiltration.

With complete freedom to run the personal training program as I saw fit, I put into practice even more efficient dollar-yielding techniques that I teach in *Personal Trainers' Guide to Earning Top Dollar*. At the new facility, I used charity challenges, testimonial campaigns, automated form design, corporate-wellness programs, exercise as medicine, connecting with college internship programs, and physician networking to rise in the ranks as easily the highest earning personal trainer in the region, with an enormous array of income streams. Understanding the importance of expert status and using the resources from this successful business, I pursued certifications in sports nutrition, bike fitting, and endurance coaching, while simultaneously gaining practical knowledge and experience in the specialized niche market of triathlon.

With all these irons in the fire, I found myself running out of time. Despite raking in large amounts of money, I was still working many personal hours to keep everything operating smoothly. I had to learn how to automate my lifestyle—so I did. And I'll teach you how to do it yourself. Over the next two years, I launched eight separate websites with cutting-edge search engine optimization; designed four new book/DVD information product packages; hired a team of inexpensive virtual assistants; and invented a blog, a podcast, and an online viral video marketing campaign using free YouTube® and Google® tools. I formed a relationship with several different nutritional and supplement companies as money-making affiliates; launched a network marketing campaign; licensed my ideas, legally protected my information products, and the list goes on. I'll teach all of it to you in *Personal Trainers' Guide to Earning Top Dollar*.

The chapters in *Personal Trainers' Guide to Earning Top Dollar* are organized on a topic-by-topic basis, so that you can immediately flip to whichever subject most interests you. If you want to focus on secret money-making techniques of face-to-face training sessions, refer to Chapter 1. If you're anxious to read about the very easy steps to beginning your online-training business, then read Chapter 8. To learn the entire spectrum of income streams available as a personal trainer, read the book cover-to-cover. The choice is yours.

How much money can you make as a normal personal trainer? Probably a maximum of $80,000 per year, and you'll be lucky if you even have a life with as many traditional one-on-one client hours as it will take. More likely, you'll top out at $40,000 to $50,000 if you want any free time. But how much money can you make as a top dollar personal trainer, using the techniques outlined in *Personal Trainers' Guide to Earning Top Dollar*? The sky is the limit. The following illustrates how your typical day might look as a top-dollar trainer:

- Wake at 8 am, open your computer, download your online information product-processing reports from four websites and transfer $400 per website into your personal bank account.
- Work out
- Perform three 30-minute nutrition and fitness phone consultations at $100 each.
- Respond to a handful of online training client Q&As at $20 per e-mail.
- Eat lunch
- Speak for 45 minutes at a corporate wellness event with 300 attendees, at two dollars a head.
- Meet two clients at their home gyms for $200 an hour.
- Go out to dinner, catch a movie or a basketball game, and head home.
- Take the next day off.

Does this scenario sound better than working at a gym eight hours a day? If so, you're ready to *train for top dollar*. Whether you're a personal trainer, gym owner, or aspiring fitness professional, this book is for you. Train smart, train hard, and keep reading.

1

Face-to-Face

In this chapter, you'll learn about how to enhance the financial effectiveness of your face-to-face training sessions, the accepted industry standard for personal training, and the bread and butter for most trainers. I'll tell you about fee structure and give you a method that will keep you automatically generating revenue and never having to re-sell clients. Highly effective time-management techniques like work-out templating are outlined, along with group-training business structure, the best method of accepting payments, how to create a corporate structure, the tips and tricks to an "instant-sell" consultation, how to conduct your personal-training sessions to keep the client coming back for more every single time, and a final chapter-ending tip that may turn out to be your biggest moneymaker yet.

Fee Structure

To begin, I will discuss the psychology and practical logistics of charging for your personal training services. Typically, your client will meet with you for a free consultation, then, if you have a "successful" consultation, and impress the client with a fun fitness fact, scary mortality statistic, or nifty card trick, he will sign up for one personal-training session or a series of packaged personal-training sessions (usually discounted, based on the number of sessions purchased). This is what I call the *hourly fee structure.*

Before delving into the specifics of exactly how to structure your consultations and face-to-face training sessions, it's going to be necessary for you to get something through your head: *The standard hourly fee structure sucks.* If you work for a gym, the client pays the gym, and then the gym pays you. Although you might receive a commission on the personal-training package purchase, if the client purchases 10 sessions and then decides to quite training after six sessions, you're robbed of four hours of potential training (that you sold).

You then combine this problem with another problem. If you work for yourself in a private studio, or are using a model in which you receive the personal training fees directly, then you're setting yourself up to get paid by the hour. While this may seem like an agreeable scenario, it gives your client the impression that they only pay you when they see you—a set hourly rate. You must instead convince your client that you are working for them 24-7, even when they're sleeping, and thus your services should be paid for using the same method that the client might use to lease a car, rent a house, or join a book club. That's right—they pay for your services on a weekly, bi-weekly, monthly, bi-monthly, or yearly basis, just as if you are the "membership" that they are purchasing. I call this the *membership fee structure.* Figure 1-1 is an example of how I set up my personal membership fee structure.

Home Personal-Training Monthly Fee Schedule			
Training session frequency	One-month commitment	Three-month commitment	Six-month commitment
3x/week	$1200	$1140	$1080
2x/week	$800	$760	$720
1x/week	$400	$380	$360
Bi-monthly	$200	$190	$180
Monthly	$100	$95	$90

Figure 1-1

The table in Figure 1-1 is fairly easy to interpret. Suppose a client wants a three-month membership and wants to see you twice per week. The charge is $760 per month (since my particular state charges a business-occupation tax, I add tax to this value).

But wait! Can't a client simply figure out that $760 divided by eight times per month comes out to $95 per session? Absolutely. I can't tell you the number of times some 40-year-old baby boomer has whipped out her purse calculator to perform this very calculation. And can't that same client think aloud about taking her business down the street, where trainer X charges a flat $60 per session? Yes, they can and they will, and your response should be something like the following:

> "Mrs. Jones, I understand that's $30/$40/$50 more than what trainer X is charging for a session. But you're not paying for that single session. You also have unlimited e-mail and phone access to me. I'll also be helping you track your diet, you can call me from the grocery store to ask me nutritional label questions, and I'll supply you with workouts for when you're away traveling and when you're not training with me. Each day, I'll oversee every aspect of each step to achieving _____ (your six-pack for Mexico, low back pain elimination, your first 5K, etc.)…"

Get the idea? This is very important—you must use this magical key phrase: "This is a *concierge personal-training service*. Nobody else offers it." You must use the word "concierge" and you must describe your services as highly unique.

Does this plan sound like complicated and involved training? Do you know how many of my clients actually call me from the grocery store? That's right, none. Do you know how many e-mails I receive on a daily basis from face-to-face clients? Perhaps two or three. Do you know how many travel workouts I have to write? None (because

I use speed templating). As a matter of fact, about as involved as my plan gets is the weekly "concierge" phone call or e-mail I'll send to each client. For example, I might send an anemic client a recipe for an iron-booster salad or a triathlete client a good article on ocean swimming. That's literally all it takes.

What if a client misses one of their monthly face-to-face personal training sessions? It doesn't matter. You see, they're paying for the membership, not the sessions. The sessions are just part of the entire package. If they don't show up for a session, they're simply opting not to use that aspect of their membership. As a matter of fact, my "concierge" style membership-based personal-training service has me devoting fewer hours of face-to-face training than any of my peers, especially because I combine it with the highly effective time *management techniques* discussed in the next section.

Time Management

Shorter Sessions

Guess what? There is no law that requires a personal training session to last 60 minutes. No research exists that shows that an hour of exercise with a trainer is superior or inferior to any other period of time. Yet, trainers almost universally insist on allowing a client to take a full hour of actual face-to-face "training" time, then spend another 5 to 10 minutes before (often longer) prepping workouts, and another 5 to 10 minutes afterward, taking notes, preparing for the next client, and getting a quick bite to eat. By the end of the day, you are devoting up to 90 minutes to each actual session and often missing out on three to five compensated training sessions that you could have performed.

The problem lies in the actual mental approach to the session, which is the same approach that was discussed in the previous section. The "face-to-face session" with the trainer is not the Holy Grail of personal training. It is very important that both you and your client understand that *the client is not paying for the session. The client is paying for you, and the membership that gains access to your knowledge and expertise.* So it doesn't matter if the sessions last 50 minutes, 40 minutes, or even 30 minutes. Use that face-to-face time to accomplish whatever fits the plan for that day. And if you've set up your session properly, that plan won't include a full 60 minutes of training. I use the following techniques to ensure that a client isn't taking up an entire hour:

- Assign a "workout challenge" that you know will only take 30 to 40 minutes to accomplish. The client must perform the workout at their maximum sustainable pace, and when they're finished, they're done. Often, your client will be proud that they "get" to leave 20 minutes early for having completed a high-quality, high-intensity workout.

- When the client shows up, send him out to warm-up on their own, while you clean up and take notes from your previous client (same with the cool-down).

- Do not set a pattern of every session being a "workout." Sometimes, I will simply sit and talk with a client about nutrition, lifestyle management, or how they managed their assigned workouts for that week. You'd be surprised at the number of people who are highly satisfied with a 30-minute sit-down chat.

- Remove all clocks from the training area, except your watch. Your client needs to understand that time is not important unless you're testing them, for example, the maximum number of push-ups in two minutes. Remember that they're paying by the week or month or year, and not by the session.

- During the sale of the personal-training membership package, if a client asks "how long" a typical session lasts, I simply tell them, "As long as it takes to finish our goals for that day." Leave it at that. Most people never follow up with, "So how long is that?" If they do, I'll give them a time range of 30 to 60 minutes, then explain that I spend quite a bit of time outside of that range prepping sessions, researching their goals, and attending to their concierge membership. Granted, because I've used strategies such as templating, article clipping, and self-education, the actual time spent outside the session is very low.

- To save time writing workouts before and after the session, have a workout theme for the day or week, and simply adapt to each client. For example, one day you can superset your trainees through four back-to-back sets that give a full-body workout. Other themes that I use include: cable/elastic-band workouts, strength power-combo workouts, core-only workouts, outdoor workouts, timed set workouts, push/pull workouts, and stability ball-only workouts. Then you simply adapt the daily theme for that client's specific goals and limitations. For example, on stability-ball day, John, the stand-out football player, would have a single-arm stability-ball chest press, stability-ball clap push-ups, and stability-ball standing squats, while Mary, the arthritic baby-boomer, would have stability ball crunches, stability ball wall squats, and a seated stability ball shoulder press. This keeps things interesting for you and fun for your clients, while saving tons of time writing workouts outside of the actual session time.

- Prep for the next client during the current client's session. Make sure you constantly have a clipboard on hand, so you can take notes on your current client, while planning your next client's workout.

- Always finish with something special. It is a great way to give a concrete ending to a session and send the message to your client that they are done, rather than hemming and hawing an extra 5 or 10 minutes. For example, when Ted finishes his last set of push-ups and stands up exhausted, I'll have him shrug and inhale, then release the shoulder tension and exhale. We'll do this exercise three times, exhaling fully on the last time and shaking all the tension out of the hands. Then I simply hold out a fist, give him a pound, and say, "See you Friday." The message is clearly sent—he's done.

Of course, seeing only one client at a time is subpar time management to begin with. Later in this chapter, I'll tell you how to enhance your training with multiple clients, sample fee structure models, camp/clinic structures, and group-training approaches. Before I discuss those approaches, it is important to talk about the second important component of time management, which is *speed templating*.

Speed Templating

I have a special folder in my computer labeled "workouts." For the first two years of personal training, I saved every workout that I ever assigned a client, and gave it a basic description. Although that folder has morphed into a massive library of diet and meal-plan templates, flexibility-program templates, diabetes-program templates, and any specific niche topics I've ever found reason to save, it now allows me to simply plug and play nearly *every* client I see into a previously written program.

It is important to remember that when speed templating, it is important to stay away from handwritten notes scrawled on a notepad and kept in some special client folder. Instead, write that client's workouts in a word or text document, and save it as two files. For example, Henry, a middle-aged male, comes to me wanting to get in shape for tennis and to lose weight. I'll save Henry's workout file as HenryXSummer2008Workouts.doc, and also as MiddleAgeMaleTennisWeightLoss.doc.

The first file goes into Henry's electronic folder on my computer, and the second file goes into my general workouts file. Either file is very accessible via an easy keyword search function on my computer. The following lists just the numeric portion of my workout-templates folder:

- 2basicworkoutswithpictures.doc
- 2dayaweekfullbodymachines.doc
- 2dayaweekfullbodymachinesandfreeweights.doc
- 2dayaweeksupersetworkout.doc
- 2dayaweekworkingmanweightworkout.doc
- 2supersetworkouts.doc

- 3-4daytoningweightloss.doc
- 3-4daytoningweightloss2.doc
- 3-5daysaweekwomentoningprogramwithpictures.doc
- 3dayaweekfullbody.doc
- 3dayaweekhighschoolswimmer.doc
- 3daysaweekbasicplan.doc
- 3daysaweekbeginnersroutine.doc
- 3dayweektoningdifficult.doc
- 3weekweightcircuitcyle5daysaweek#2.doc
- 3weekweightcircuitcyle5daysaweek.doc
- 4dayaweekworkoutintermediate.doc
- 5-6daysaweekrunnersworkout.doc
- 5-6daysaweekrunnersworkout2.doc
- 5daysaweekbasiccoreroutines.doc
- 5daysaweekbasicroutine.doc
- 5daysaweekfullbodysupersets.doc
- 5daysaweeksupersetcircuitsandcardiointervals.doc
- 6daysaweekmuscularstrengthandenduranceandcardio.doc
- 7dayaweekfullbodyforgirl.doc
- 7daysaweektheVPROGRAM.doc
- 7weekcyclebasic.doc
- 7weekcyclewithintroandvariety.doc
- 8week6daysaweek#1.doc
- 8week6daysaweek#2.doc
- 8week6daysaweek#3.doc
- 8week6daysaweek#4.doc
- 8weekfitnessprogram5daysaweek.doc
- 8weekfitnessprogramforskinnywomen.doc
- 8weekprogram3daysaweek.doc
- 8weekprogram4weekcircuit4weekweights5daysaweek.doc

If you start templating now, in about three months, it will start to pay off, and two years from now, you may find that you never have to write another workout. You can even sell your templates to fellow personal trainers or online clients. Let's move past the individual personal training session time management into another highly effective time management and income yielding technique, which is *multi-person training*.

Group Training

Most trainers who do any amount of personal research have by now heard of the group-training benefits and perhaps implemented group training themselves. Of course, the value of training more than one individual is readily apparent—charge a lower price per individual but make an overall greater income, due to the number of actual paying customers. The three most effective ways that I've successfully utilized group training are boot camp, semi-private training, and niche camp/clinic models.

Boot Camp

- In the summer of 2006 and 2007, I would roll out of bed twice a week at 6 am to work out in the park. Perhaps this subject falls under the time management section, because, you must understand, I was going out to get a fantastic workout, and it just so happened that people were meeting me there to workout with me, and they were paying. As a matter of fact, 15 to 20 people were paying $10 to show up and *do my workout* with me. While there are many variations on the theme, this park was essentially just a boot camp. In one popular workout, I'd show up with a few decks of cards, gather everyone together, assign partners, and then have the partners deal each other a card from the deck. Number cards were a 10-yard sprint for whichever number appeared (i.e., 2=20 yards, 9=90 yards), jacks were 30 seconds of push-ups, queens were 60 seconds of squats, kings were 15 partner crunches...you get the idea. Then we'd just set the clock for 20 minutes and go. Each workout included a 10-minute warm-up jog and stretch and a five-minute cool-down jog and stretch. The beauty of this model is that it was simply a bunch of friends working out in the park. Sure, they all signed waivers (discussed later in this chapter) and paid into a small cigar box that I laid out on a picnic bench, but there were *zero overhead costs*. Don't worry about renting the park, as most city park systems don't care that early in the morning. Just make sure you know the sprinkler schedule.

- How to market your boot camp:

  ✓ Post flyers for boot camp in community locations. The most effective locations are: grocery store, library, health club, park, or mall. Include the day and time (use a regular time, like every Tuesday and Thursday at 6 am). Choose times before or after work, or during lunch hour.

  ✓ My advertisement had a picture of me standing with folded arms and a wide stance, and included a caption that read, "Get in the best shape of your life. Ben's Boot Camp. All levels and ages welcome." Under that caption were the location, time, and my phone number.

✓ It is important to note that if you have an online presence (discussed more in Chapter 4), include the URL for the boot-camp section of your website (i.e., bengreenfieldfitness.com/bootcamp). In that section, simply post the *title* of the planned workout, using this title as a teaser. For example, in the deck of cards workout previously listed, I simply wrote for that week's online posting: Boot Camp Workout of the Week: Poker in the Park.

✓ Include incentives during the boot camp series that allow individuals to get their money back (i.e., Boot camp MVP; attend nine, Get one free; most push-ups performed, etc.). People love motivation to save money..

✓ Save all the workouts in the boot camp template folder on your computer and recycle them the following year.

Semi-Private Training

• I use this model quite frequently for two to four individuals. For example, Bill wants a weekly trainer but can't afford the $400 per month membership fee. How do I know this? He told me during a phone inquiry that he wanted to train, but just couldn't handle the price. As any good salesman should do, I simply quipped back, "Two other people called just this week and said the same thing, so let me tell you about our special, limited-time offer for semi-private training." (It might not be limited time, but people like to think they just barely snuck in at the last moment. Remember, folks love a good deal).

• I then introduce Bill to a very simple model in which he shows up at the studio or gym at the same time as Cindy and Greg, and each of them pays one third the normal membership cost of training. They do the same workout together, as a circuit, with varying levels of weight and reps, based on their fitness levels and desired goals. The carrot at the end of the stick is that they don't receive the same concierge-style service as my individual clients, and I make sure they know it. Drop one-liners like, "My personal training client, Ted, called me yesterday because he was having a really difficult time with sugar cravings and wanted to know what would curb a carbohydrate appetite, so we talked about that for awhile." You'd be surprised how many times you'll hear a semi-private client say, "I'm about ready to bump it up to the next level of personal training." You'll also be surprised when you see how many of them actually do it. It is more than you think, considering they were about to take their business elsewhere just four to six weeks prior.

• I have a similar corporate gym personal training model that closely approximates semi-private training. For four weeks, a corporate group of 8 to 12 employees can work with me, "a fitness and diet expert," at the corporate-site gym or health facility.

The entire group meets with a personal trainer for a group exercise program once a week for one hour. If desired, you can actually set up the pricing to allow for each member of the group to also receive a private 20 to 30 minute meeting with a trainer once a week during this four-week time span. It is best to price this bid as a one shot deal, because corporations like a set bid on corporate training. For the aforementioned description, with group training only, I charge $2100 (that's four hours of my time). The private training sessions are priced at $50 (but last a *maximum* of 30 minutes) and are paid out-of-pocket, not through the corporate-wellness program.

- With semi-private training, whether studio, gym, or corporate based, you'll find that a good portion of the individuals actually sign up for individual private training, once their series of semi-private training is done. Plus, these sessions can be far more socially exciting with multiple conversations and different personalities.

Niche Camp/Clinic

- Niche marketing is discussed more comprehensively in Chapter 10, but essentially involves targeting a very specific population with your services or information products. Whereas a general fitness feature like a boot camp can involve the shotgun-marketing approach previously mentioned, like plastering the local town hot spots with flyers, a niche camp or clinic can involve very targeted marketing and you can often charge a much higher amount for the actual event.

- For example, my niche demographic is the *endurance athlete population*, and more specifically, triathletes. This allows me to target the local triathlon community with narrowed subject matter events, such as the following:
    - ✓ Open-water swim clinics (drafting, sighting, cold-water swimming, wetsuits, etc.)
    - ✓ Transition clinics (how to effectively swim-to-bike and bike-to-run)
    - ✓ Two to three day cycling camps (involves two to three group rides of 30 to 80 miles)
    - ✓ Course specific rides and runs (i.e., learn the strategies for ironman Coeur D' Alene, run the Spokane half marathon course, etc.)
    - ✓ Endurance nutrition seminars (fueling for Ironman, ergogenic aids, etc.)

- It's very easy to market your niche product. In my case (in addition to my online newsletter marketing and e-mail lists), I utilize the free training calendars in local outdoor magazines, the local cycling and triathlon store bulletin boards, and triathlon club forums and club meetings.

- You can even more specifically target your market by offering a discount to certain clubs. Once again, people love a good deal, and if they feel they're getting a bargain discount, you'll see repeat customers at each of your niche market clinics.

Other group-training models exist, but the boot camp, semi-private training, and niche camp/clinic models have been tried and proven. They are guaranteed moneymakers. On the subject of making money, I will discuss how it actually ends up in your hands. Before I move on to *collecting* money, I'd like to share one of my top time-management tips for expanding your knowledge-base as a fitness professional. I call it the *one-read rule*.

> *The One-Read Rule*: Only glance at a piece of paper once—period. This rule includes articles, magazines, and e-mail newsletters. Don't open a piece of mail and then set it aside to read later. Instead, do a glance-over. If there is important information, memorize it, or write it down. If it is not important, throw it away. You would not believe the amount of time that you probably waste when you "repeat-read." For practice, don't go back and read this tip—just move along.

Once you've established your expert status with these techniques, you'll have people constantly knocking at your door to hire you to apply your knowledge in helping them achieve their goals. But you must be ready to take the money.

Accepting Payments

At some point in the personal training process, money has to change hands. Your clients have to pay you. Hopefully, you now understand the importance of the client not paying on a "session-by-session" or a package-session basis, but rather paying a regular membership fee for training. But *how* should you actually accept payments?

The most important rule to follow when charging your client is that *they must not be reminded that they're paying*. That's right—you never end a three-, or five-, or 10-session package and then come back to the client begging for more. No one likes to remember that they're paying a membership fee or being charged for a service subscription. For example, if you subscribe to a magazine one time, for two years, receive the magazine, enjoy it, and are never reminded about paying, you're typically a satisfied customer. If, however, you go to the grocery store to purchase the magazine each month, or just get a three-month subscription, and every magazine comes with a big bold headline threatening to cut off your subscription unless you renew soon, you'll be a less than satisfied customer.

This is why you'll want to be running an automatic debit or credit system with automated recurring payments to make the payment process invisible. The only time your client will see it is when he reviews his monthly credit-card statement (and most people rarely do that).

If you're not currently set-up to process credit cards, then you need to be. I like to avoid clumsy physical credit-card terminals. They can only be in one location and that will often hold you back. Instead, use an online virtual credit card terminal service. I use the following process:

- When a client signs up for training, the activity waiver includes the following paragraph:

    I understand that I have paid or am obligated to pay Ben Greenfield a negotiated fee for this activity, and that under no circumstances is any of this amount refundable. I agree to commit to training with Ben Greenfield for _____ (months/years) and agree to pay Ben Greenfield a fee of _____ per (week/month/year) for my participation in this activity. To not be charged for a meeting, I understand that I am required to give a 24-hour notice of cancellation for any meeting with Ben Greenfield. If I decide not to engage in a training program, I agree to pay a consultation fee of $100 for my initial meeting with Ben Greenfield. If I desire my payments to be automatically deducted via a credit- or debit-card payment, I will supply the following information:

    card type: _____; card #: _____;

    card expiration date: _____; name on card:

    _____.

- When the clients fill out the waiver, I'll remind them about perks, such as airline miles, rewards points, and increasing their credit score when they use their credit card for recurring transactions. People love to be reminded of little bonus features.

- I then use a combination of two online services. The first service is http://www.1shoppingcart.com, which is the same provider that I use to run my online affiliate programs, ad campaigns, newsletters, e-mail lists, e-books, and web-based shopping cart. It runs about 50 to 100 dollars per month, depending on the services chosen. The second service is http://www.authorize.net, which is my service for actually processing credit cards via my web-based shopping cart.

Authorize.net takes a percentage of the actual transaction, which varies depending on your account, but is usually well worth the service provided. Most importantly, the authorize.net system can also serve as a stand-alone virtual terminal in which you can process the credit card number that the client provides on the signed waiver. Voila! You can now run your client's credit card information from an online secure server anywhere in the world, and set up the transaction as a recurring transaction so that you don't ever have to worry about doing it twice.

- I keep the signed waivers in a secure, locked location, with the client's health-history forms and personal information. Everything is very secure, and none of my clients have ever had an issue with fraud or suspicious credit-card activity with this system.

Bartering

Any discussion of accepting payments wouldn't be complete without mentioning one of the most beautiful and tax-free payment methods, which is *bartering*. Never forget that the dollar is technically worthless, as it is no longer backed by gold. However, physical goods are legitimate forms of ensuring that both parties find a transaction agreeable, and I've always taken advantage of bartering as both a tool for negotiating prices on personal training, negotiating prices on goods and services, and for saving on taxes. While the value of these bartered services or goods should be reported to the IRS, bartering will give both you and your client leverage for arranging transactions. The following list includes most of my bartered deals:
- Free haircuts (barber)
- Books (avid reader who had books I wanted)
- Wine and champagne (wine aficionado)
- Fancy dinners (restaurant owner)
- A carbon racing bicycle (triathlete)
- An appraisal on a condo (appraiser)
- Chiropractic care (chiropractor)
- Massage therapy (massage therapist)
- A home water filter (wellness network marketer)
- Supplements (nutrition network marketer)
- And my personal favorite: two highly discounted homes (homebuilder)

Just ask yourself, *does my client have goods or services that I'm willing to trade personal-training services for?* If so, don't hesitate to pull the trigger on this method. It usually results in two very satisfied parties.

Business Structure

With all this flow of money and goods, it is important to make an examination of an important component of your personal training career —the DBA: Doing Business As. If you're truly serious about wanting to make the big bucks as a trainer, you're eventually going to need move out from underneath the umbrella of a gym or health club W2 form and operate more independently as a recognizable and legal business entity. Make it simple, because you only really need to worry about two main problems: *tax and liability*. I've operated as both an LLC (limited-liability company) and as a sole proprietor, and each has advantages and disadvantages.

LLC

- An LLC is easier to form and has less paperwork and hassle than a regular corporation, like an S corporation. When you form an LLC, you are legally separating your personal assets from your business assets. *This factor is significant from a liability standpoint.* The importance is that if a client gets injured and decides to sue you, they can't take your home, your personal bank account, etc. Only your business assets are at stake.

- In addition, when you own an LLC, the profits or losses of the business pass directly through to the owner's personal income tax return and are not taxed as corporate earnings. *This factor is significant from a tax standpoint.* It is called pass-through taxation and means that, compared to a regular corporation, you're not paying taxes twice (once through your business and once through your personal income). Interestingly, taxes on LLCs vary considerably from state to state, and you aren't required to form an LLC in the state in which you are doing business (especially if you're running an online-training business). Nevada, for example, is far more business friendly than Washington when it comes to business taxes.

- Since most trainers work on their own, you would be the sole owner and member of your LLC, although you could eventually hire employees in the future or take on additional members in your LLC (a distribution of the profits is shared among each member according to their percentage ownership). *If you plan on expanding your business by hiring other trainers or employees*, which I discuss in Chapter 5 when I talk about outsourcing, *then you'll want to form an LLC.*

- Most personal training certification organizations offer insurance programs for sole proprietorships, but many do not offer business liability insurance programs for LLCs, so you may need to venture outside your organization to insure your business.

- Ultimately, an LLC is going take more paperwork and leave you spending quite a bit of time organizing your quarterly business taxes, since you'll be filing. I highly recommend purchasing a copy of Quickbooks and considering quarterly advice from a certified accountant or even hiring a CPA when running your LLC.

Sole Proprietor

- To legally run your business as a sole proprietor, you must file a "doing business as" form with your local county, which will then provide you with a special tax identification number for your business. You can do business as yourself, under your name, or you can name your business anything you'd like, as long as it appears on your business license, which you'll be provided with after registering with your county. *Compared to an LLC, a sole proprietorship is a bit riskier from a liability standpoint, but not significantly different from a personal tax standpoint.*

- There are far fewer taxes and paperwork associated with a sole proprietorship, so less time is involved with pushing papers. When I ran a sole proprietorship, I personally payed my taxes quarterly using a 1040ES form, which allowed me to pay an estimated tax, based on the previous year's earnings. Of course, during the time between quarters when that money wasn't being used to pay taxes, I'd place it in an interest-yielding money-market account to grow a bit, prior to giving it to Uncle Sam.

- Sole proprietorships are easy to form and simple to understand. Using an online tax service as simple as http://www.turbotax.com and carrying personal liability insurance through your certification organization, you can actually operate fairly successfully with this uncomplicated model.

Most importantly, remember that no matter what business entity you decide to form, your clients *must* be given the impression of business professionalism and organization when assessing you as a personal trainer. This is a crucial component of the trust relationship. Display your business license and certifications prominently and you will be given respect, and, just as importantly, a regular paycheck from your clients.

The Consultation

First impressions will make or break you. Most personal trainers make their most serious financial mistakes during the initial consultation and meeting with a client. The most important rule is: *consultations are not free sessions.*

Whether you are a corporate gym entity or a private-training studio, your clients must value your time from the get-go, and if you advertise yourself using a "free consultation" model, you'll find that you: first, attract a high number of free-loaders who can take 5 to 10 hours each week using you for free advice; second, turn the consultation into an awkward one-on-one "sales session;" and third, if you are a gym or have trainers working under you, a large amount of money is wasted paying trainers to conduct a free session.

On the other hand, few potential clients will be willing to pay a full personal-training session price for a consultation. Therefore, whether you are a gym or private studio, I highly suggest using the following group consultations (or group "orientation" if you are a gym) model.

- Upon joining your facility or gym, or expressing an interest in personal training, a new member or potential client is given a sheet that gives details on a special new member orientation class. The sheet gives the details on topics covered (health, fitness, diet, etc.), the benefits of attending, orientation day and time, how to sign-up, and the fee. At the bottom of the sheet, there is a form that allows the new member to check which day he plans on attending, with a space to write his name and phone number. He then turns this sheet in to the front desk, or to you, along with the payment, and one to two days before the orientation, the trainer or trainers leading the group orientation call all of the signees to remind them of the class. Try to have the class at a regular day/time, and you'll be surprised at how quickly word gets around on the "new members" class, and how any potential clients bring their friends along (who also pay).

- The cost of the group orientation has a $10 to $20 per person fee, backed by an unconditional money-back guarantee. If, for any reason, anyone in attendance feels as if the session was not worth $20, they will immediately be offered a refund. This makes the orientation "risk-free" for those individuals in terms of cost. Of course, very few people ever ask for their money back.

- The main thrust of the new-member group orientation should be directed at the one simple goal that makes individuals feel that they need a trainer and will never reach their full potential without investing in a trainer. The orientation can lay out the concept of balanced fitness components (flexibility, strength, cardiovascular, neuromuscular, core, etc.), nutrition (basic weight-loss concepts), intensities (heart-rate training, choosing weights, etc.), goal-setting and baseline measurements, and then give samples of how a trainer designs a personalized program based on these components.

- The attendees of the group orientation are then presented with a form of a sale. It can be somewhat subtle, as simply a nod in the direction of a sign-up book that shows exactly which times the trainer(s) has available in his schedule, with contracts and pricing sheets readily available beside the sign-up book. Don't let people see prices, contracts, sign-up sheets, etc. until the presentation is completely finished. Should an individual want to begin training, he can fill out a contract on the spot and immediately take it to the front desk or to you for payment. If possible, add a direct-debit or credit-card option to payments, and collect automatically from clients on a weekly or monthly basis if they would like. But make sure you get all this information immediately after the class—you must reel them in while they're excited!

- You can take this concept one step further and also present a special-topics series at your facility, featuring a weekly series on topics, such as sugar, alcohol, functional training, sample-core workouts, etc. The member cost, for example, would be $8 to $10 per class, and just so members feel that they're getting a deal, non-member costs would be $15 to $20. Include an option for members to sign-up for a whole month of classes for $25 (not available for non-members). Apply the same sales thrust *after* the special-topics presentation. This way, you're not only working on the new potential clients and new members with the group orientation, but you're also working on the existing gym or studio population with the special-topics class.

- You do the math. If you implement both these classes and each lasts one hour, then at two classes per week you'd be "consulting" two hours per week and you'd be getting paid for it, which is a much better model than a series of individual free consultations. The gym doesn't pay a group of trainers a massive amount of "fit time" wages for free consultations, and the trainer is highly motivated by a group of attentive individuals and a paycheck. At a gym, split the profit from the new member group consultations and special-topics series between the gym and the trainers to cover overhead costs, printing flyers, copying handouts, etc.

On the other hand, suppose you are stuck in a situation where the free individual consultation model is the norm. Perhaps you work at an old-school gym that is stuck in its ways, or you just prefer face-to-face single consultations. I use the following model for such situations:
- Meet
    - ✓ Introductions build rapport.
    - ✓ Justify that you're going to ask questions for the client's individual benefit, do not use "generic" questions.
    - ✓ Build trust and respect.
- Learn
    - ✓ You're the student.
    - ✓ Find out the primary need of the person sitting in front of you.
    - ✓ Discover the answer to the most important question: What do they want? What are their desires and goals?
    - ✓ Find out some of the exercise/eating mistakes that individual is making.

- ✓ Ask or collect exercise history information. College/high school sports? Worked with other trainers? Like to workout outdoors?
- ✓ Ask or collect health-history information. Joint problems? Family history? Medications?
- Educate
  - ✓ You're the teacher.
  - ✓ Explain the concept of "Synergy:"
    - ⇨ Proper exercise
    - ⇨ Proper nutrition
    - ⇨ Active lifestyle
  - ✓ Explain the concept of metabolism and how it is affected by diet and exercise.
  - ✓ Explain the concept of aerobic vs. anaerobic exercise.
  - ✓ Explain the concept of functional training/core vs. isolated body-part training.
  - ✓ Explain the concept of multiple components of fitness.
    - ⇨ Cardiovascular fitness
    - ⇨ Muscular endurance
    - ⇨ Muscular strength
    - ⇨ Balance
    - ⇨ Flexibility
    - ⇨ Body composition
  - ✓ Explain the SAID principle: Specific Adaptation to Imposed Demands.
  - ✓ Explain the concept of "Bioindividuality:"
    - ⇨ Same foundational concepts of fitness
    - ⇨ Different application for different bodies
- Sell
  - ✓ Explain how you're going to take the concepts you've just discussed to design an exercise and/or nutrition program that will achieve the desires, goals, and needs of your clients as quickly, efficiently, and injury-free as possible.
  - ✓ Design a customized package that meets that individual's needs (i.e., bi-monthly nutritional/body, fat/exercise check-ups and workout changes combined with weekly trainer meetings and a concierge three-month membership to nutrition, exercise, and lifestyle management).
  - ✓ Most important: Make it customized! If they like golf, design a program that drastically cuts body fat, completely takes the guesswork out of choosing foods, and is totally golf-specific—building balance, rotational strength, and mental clarity designed to take their game to the next level.

Finally, remember that the more respect and expert authority you maintain in your field, the higher a salary you can command for you consultations. I've worked very hard on establishing an expert reputation in the fitness community, and now charge

$100 per 30 minutes for any potential client that is interested in training and wants to sit down and talk about utilizing my expertise. This automatically ensures that I am only interviewing the clients who are actually motivated to train, and turns the consultation into just that—a trainer-client interview and not a sales session.

To save time during the consultation, I've designed a series of downloadable Internet-based forms that collect each individual's health history, as well as an online printable exercise waiver. When a client calls or e-mails me to schedule a meeting, I'll direct them to this website and instruct them to print, complete, and bring the forms to our initial meeting. This is a huge timesaver, as well as a way to cut costs on printing supplies. Online forms are very simple to create, and your web-hosting service should be able to explain it to you within just a few minutes. If you run an online personal-training business, it's likely that you'll deal solely with electronic forms, meaning that the client completes the form online, presses submit, and the information ends up in your e-mail box. Personally, I prefer to deal with printable forms for my face-to-face clients, but you could potentially keep your entire information-collecting process electronic by using online forms only. I did this for some time, and would simply save the e-mails in my client's folder on my computer.

Especially when working with sensitive client health information, you must satisfy HIPPA regulations by controlling access to your computer systems, so you'll need to make sure these folders are password protected to comply with federal privacy act regulations. Visit http://en.wikipedia.org/wiki/HIPPA for a thorough explanation of HIPPA. Creating your online presence will be discussed further in Chapters 3 and 4.

The Personal-Training Session

Everyone has their own style of training and their own unique approach to the fitness process. This book's intention is to teach money-making tips, not to teach you how to train. However, the manner in which you conduct your training sessions significantly affects your client's decision on whether or not to come back for more.

Is it your intention during a personal training session to produce a repeat customer? If not, change your approach. *Your client must depend on you during each exercise session.* He should be given the impression that you are not just a "counter." You're also not a slave driver, barking instructions for the workout while standing and observing with folded arms. You must be an active part of the workout—a helper, an educator, a spotter, a trainer. Techniques that you can use to ensure that your client *needs* you in order to exercise include:

- *Using cohort exercises*: A cohort exercise is any movement or drill that requires a partner. I make a rule to include at least one cohort exercise with every session. Among my favorites are medicine-ball throwing exercises, elastic band partner-resistance exercises, and follow-the-leader obstacle courses. (A wonderful resource for partner-based games and cohort exercises is http://www.exuberantanimal.com.)

- *Educating training*: Every time we meet, I make a point to give my client a recent article or a new tip or trick on fitness. Empower your client with knowledge during the training session and he will associate it with far more value. People love to learn.

- *Reviewing nutrition*: All my clients are required to come to their training sessions with a diet logging book in hand. In our first meeting, I instruct them to go to Office Depot®, Barnes & Noble®, or any bookstore and find a log-keeping book in which they can track nutrition (keep it simple: food description, time, and amount). I also maintain a link on the member's section of my website with printable nutrition-logging forms. This way, as you analyze nutrition during the training session, you're achieving multiple goals during the training sessions, thus improving the quality of the client experience. If you're not a nutrition expert, you'll learn how to easily fix that in Chapter 7.

- *Sitting and talking about lifestyle management*: As a trainer, you must often take on the role of "psychologist." Sometimes, your clients don't need to train—they need to talk. They need encouragement, advice, and direction. *Never underestimate your ability to provide a rich and meaningful stress-reducing resource for your client*. Both stress and sleep significantly affect wellness, which are two subjects I'll bring up when we're sitting and talking prior to a session. Often, it leads to a 30-minute discussion, then I'll simply assign a workout and say goodbye.

- *Starting conversations*: Another problem is the silent session. Don't let that happen. Enjoying the workout experience is crucial for your client. My top three conversation starters are one, "What did you do this weekend?"; two, "What are you going to do this weekend?" and three, "What do you think about (the latest current event, pop culture fad, political scandal, etc.)?" The key rule to follow is that you must *ask open-ended questions* to which a simple yes or no response is impossible. This is also useful for consultations, but typically I'll ask questions like, "Why are you here?", "Tell me about your health?", and "How do you envision a personal trainer helping you?" Just one of these questions sometimes fills an entire session with good conversation.

- *Not counting*: Try to go through an entire session without counting your client's reps as it will be great practice for you to fill the time with more meaningful content than shouted numbers. Amazingly, I've found that most people count pretty well without any help.

- *Finishing with something special*: Always end by giving your client something special and meaningful to take away from the session. I highly recommend yoga as a tool for finishing a workout. I'll take a client through five or six series of yoga moves with a focus on deep diaphragmatic breathing and relaxation. At the end of the session, I'll encourage them to release all their stress and be ready to attack their tasks for the day or end the day relaxed and de-stressed. People love it. You can literally watch their eyes glaze over as stress leaves their body and all those relaxation hormones take over. If your client walks away with a body full of dopamine, they'll come back for more.

Speaking of finishing with something special, I'll finish this chapter with a final tip: a story about a very successful promotional campaign that will blow your mind with its simplicity and high earning potential. The following is a very useful strategy for picking up trainees, especially if you're new to an area and struggling to find recognition and establish a client base. I call it the *charity challenge* technique.

Final Tip

Using a newspaper or magazine advertisement, radio spot, or (my preferred method) an opt-in e-mail list (ensures you won't get filtered as spam, which is discussed more in Chapter 4), advertise your services for free to one individual, as displayed in Figure 1-2.

Dear [first name],

I am looking for one individual to train for FREE.

You must be currently out of shape, obese, and willing to undergo a full metabolic-testing profile at least once per month. You must be willing to work with a personal trainer at least once per week and follow a very specific nutritional and lifestyle program.

This is a chance of a lifetime. If you or someone you know may be interested, please contact me immediately. I will select the lucky individual in exactly one week.

Ben

Figure 1-2

After I sent out this e-mail, I was barraged with over 200 e-mails, phone calls, and inquiries from the local community. People submitted pictures, and bios, desperate to be the "chosen one." Friends told friends that Ben Greenfield was training for free and word spread like wildfire.

Beautiful! In exchange for one hour per week of my time training for free, *I had a very personal marketing contact list of every single person in town who wanted to use my services* (I subsequently sold personal training to nearly 25% of the individuals on that list).

In the ensuing series of months, I sent out a bi-weekly update on the progress, diet, workouts, and exercise program of my chosen individual. More and more people signed up for training as they witnessed this person undergo a total-body transformation via e-mail newsletter and online pictures and stories.

If you go to http://www.pacificfit.net/newsletters.html and access the newsletter archives for May of 2007, the title of this charity challenge was Total Body Transformation. There are a series of newsletters that cover the topic, so you can see exactly how I structured my follow-up reports. My "free" trainee became a full time client! This method is just one inventive way for filling up your weekly schedule with quality clientele. Chapter 2 reveals an even more effective and highly professional way to network your way into the weight-loss community.

2

Physician Networking

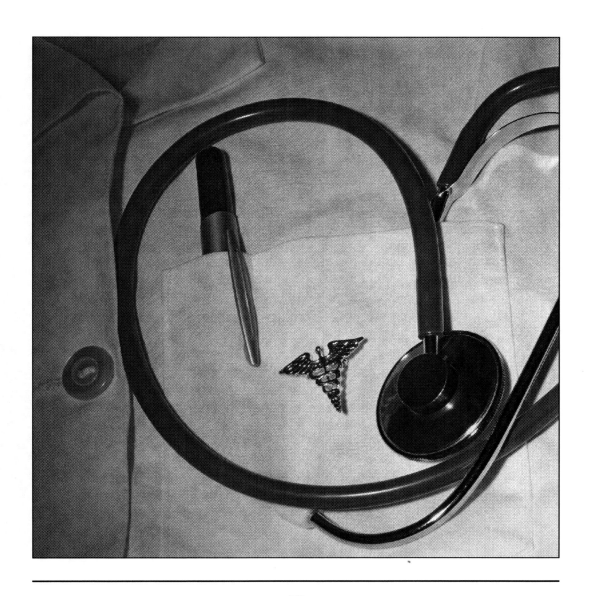

Over 40 million Americans face the direct threat of metabolic disease due to their lifestyle patterns. Each of these individuals is going to end up seeing a physician. Do you have a system in place for a smoothly operating physician-to-trainer and trainer-to-physician client-referral system? This chapter explains why a new directive from the American College of Sports Medicine and American Medical Association is going to pay big dividends for trainers who are ready, and gives you the exact forms, letters, and instructions you'll need to be optimally prepared for the flow of patient referrals and one giant step ahead of the game.

It amazes me that physician networking has rarely been explored by the personal-training community. Consider the following November 5, 2007 press release from the American College of Sports Medicine and the American Medical Association:

For immediate release Nov. 5, 2007:

WASHINGTON, D.C. – The American College of Sports Medicine (ACSM) and the American Medical Association (AMA) today launched Exercise is Medicine™, a new program designed to encourage America's patients to incorporate physical activity and exercise into their daily routine. Exercise is Medicine calls on doctors to prescribe exercise to their patients.

A recent survey conducted of the public by ACSM found that nearly two-thirds of patients (65%) would be more interested in exercising to stay healthy if advised by their doctor and given additional resources. Four out of 10 physicians (41%) talk to their patients about the importance of exercise, but don't always offer suggestions on the best ways to be physically active. Patients (25%) look to their doctor first for advice on exercise and physical activity. They turn next to fitness and health websites (24%).

The goal of the Exercise is Medicine program is to encourage physicians to record physical activity as a vital sign during patient visits. Able patients will be advised to participate in at least 30 minutes of physical activity and 10 minutes of stretching and light muscle training five days a week.

A new website—www.exerciseismedicine.org—contains educational materials and tool kits for physicians to use in their practices. The site also includes information for patients, the media, and policymakers, as well as a listing of initial supporting organizations. Educational models will be developed for use in medical schools so students can learn the importance of prescribing exercise to patients early in their careers.

Physical inactivity is a fast-growing public health problem in this country and contributes to a variety of chronic diseases and health complications, including obesity, coronary artery disease, diabetes, high blood pressure, cancer, depression and anxiety, arthritis, and osteoporosis. In addition to improving a patient's overall health, increasing physical activity has proven effective in the treatment and prevention of chronic disease.

"We already advise against smoking; recommending exercise should be no different," said Robert E. Sallis, M.D., ACSM president. "Physicians can support the program by prescribing exercise and offering patients basic educational materials. Exercise can have tremendous health benefits for patients."

"More than half of Americans don't get nearly enough exercise and would be astounded to see how much difference a brisk 30-minute walk a few times a week makes in their overall health," said Ronald M. Davis, M.D., AMA president. "We encourage physicians to talk to their patients about the importance of exercise and to work with them to establish programs they can start today and continue throughout their lives."

Exciting! Imagine the 40-plus million overweight and obese individuals in this country being informed that they *must* engage in exercise. You'd be surprised at the number of physicians who currently *aren't* encouraging their patients to exercise, or at least weren't until this announcement from the AMA and ACSM.

Because I work in close contact with physicians in my medical exercise facility, I knew of this announcement some months prior to its release, and had comprehensive marketing material prepared to send to the entire local physician community in December 2007. Figure 2-1 is my introductory letter, which was attached to a business card with full contact information.

Notice that the letter references nutritional services. If you don't currently include nutrition services, then I highly recommend pursuing a degree or certification. This is one education that will pay you dividends. (Refer to Chapter 7 for more details.) This letter should also include an authorization of release of medical information form and a physician's approval form, such as that given in Figure 2-2 and Figure 2-3.

Dear Dr. _____,

As a wellness professional providing health, nutrition, and fitness services directly in the _____ community, I offer a complete chronic-disease management package for overweight and obese individuals. This program includes preventive measures for individuals who struggle with excess weight, metabolic syndrome, and resistance to proper exercise. My comprehensive approach utilizes a combination of nutritional counseling, lifestyle coaching, and exercise-program design. By adopting a synergistic approach to address the multiple challenges facing the overweight or obese patient, we provide a successful environment for reducing chronic disease risk factors while improving wellness.

- We use the following procedures in our approach:
- Resting metabolic rate calculation
- Flexibility, strength, and cardiovascular-endurance testing
- Body composition determination
- Nutritional consulting and meal-plan design
- Personal training and exercise-program design
- Lifestyle wellness coaching

Research has shown that the combined approach of proper fitness and nutrition management can reduce multiple risk factors associated with obesity, such as hypertension, high cholesterol, type II diabetes, heart disease, stroke, and arthritis. By working with my facility on a referral basis, you can provide an effective disease management program for your patients.

You can contact me at any time to enroll any patient. To satisfy HIPPA regulations, I have enclosed an authorization of release of medical information, as well as a physician's approval form. You may copy and utilize these documents during our interaction. I look forward to working with you.

Sincerely,

_____

Figure 2-1

Authorization for Release of Medical Information: Personal Training

I hereby authorize_____
to release the following information from the medical record of:
Patient's name _____
Address _____
Telephone _____
Date of birth _____

Information to be released:
(If specific treatment dates are not indicated, information from the most recent visit will be released.)
Exercise testing
Medical history and physical exam
Physiology/biomechanics lab procedures
Nutritional consultation
Laboratory results (specify) _____
Other (specify) _____

Information to be released to:
Name of person/organization _____
Address _____
Telephone _____

Purpose of disclosure information:
_____

I do not give permission for disclosure or disclosure of this information other than that specified above.

I request that this consent become invalid 90 days from the date I sign it or a different date specified here: _____. I understand that this consent can be revoked at any time, except to the extent that disclosure made in good faith has already occurred in reliance of this consent.

Patient's signature _____
Date _____
Witness _____
Signature _____

Figure 2-2

Physician's Approval Form for Exercise

Please complete this form and return via fax to _____
at fax number _____. Thank you!

_____ has medical approval to participate in fitness programs and in the use of exercise equipment at various sites, including home or office, that may be provided by and/or recommended by the staff of _____ _____ personal-training program.

Choose the appropriate recommendation for your patient:

_____ Patient is cleared to exercise without restriction.

_____ Patient is cleared to exercise with the following restrictions or guidelines. Please include the exercise heart rate and/or MET level desired for your patient. If a graded exercise test was performed, please include results if available. _____

_____

_____Patient is not cleared to exercise.

Physician signature:_____

Physician name (print):_____

Date:_____

Address:_____

Phone:_____

Fax:_____

E-mail:_____

Figure 2-3

I followed this letter with a personal phone call to the office of each physician. The best time to call is prior to 8 am, when the doctor is in the office but is not yet seeing patients, during the lunch hour, and *not* after 5 pm when they're trying to rush out and will be annoyed when you call.

I would make each call short and sweet, "Hi, this is Ben Greenfield. I understand you're probably busy with patients, but I just wanted to make sure that you received my letter about the exciting new fitness and nutrition program I'm offering for chronic disease management. It's just a free referral service where I take on your patients and teach them how to exercise and eat properly."

Pause here for an answer. They either received the letter or didn't, but either way, continue...

"Would you mind just quickly jotting my cell/office phone number down for your office manager to schedule patient consultations at my training studio/gym?"

Finish with, "So, anytime you have a patient that needs to exercise or needs diet management, I can work cooperatively with you to oversee his program, and, of course, we satisfy all HIPPA regulations in our procedures. Thanks for your time, doctor. I look forward to helping."

That's it! About two percent of the personal trainers in your community are making these calls right now, usually because they haven't yet learned to work cooperatively with the medical system, or because they don't have access to the few simple documents that you now have. Hopping on the *Exercise as Medicine* bandwagon and using the scenario of harvesting your client population from the local medical community is truly the wave of the future for personal trainers to make some serious bucks.

Not only does http://www.exerciseismedicine.org now feature a rich array of resources to help you network with the medical community, including selected articles from ACSM's Health and Fitness Journal to give to your clients, and various books in support of the Exercise as Medicine movement, but they also include, on the website, a complete kit for health and fitness professionals to network with their local physician community. Go to the website and click on Health and Fitness Professionals.

This entire movement is entirely supported by funding from the AMA, the ACSM, and the office of the surgeon general. What does this factor mean to you? Our nation's medical professionals and government are taking this seriously, and you are a key cog in the wheel set.

By using the aforementioned resources, you'll open the door to hundreds, and, depending on the size of your community, potentially thousands of patients who have been ordered to exercise by a physician. These are desperate people who need you to save or vastly improve the quality their lives, and they're willing to pay for it!

Will your personal training services ever be covered by insurance? To date, no billing codes exist for this situation. But I strongly believe that in the near future, health insurance will actually cover the cost of fitness prescription in the same manner that it currently covers often needless procedures such as gastric-bypass surgery. *If an insurance company can pay over a hundred thousand dollars for a surgery, then three to six months of personal training could certainly be justified.*

If you have already networked into your local medical community, you'll be ahead of the game and ready for action when this change happens. In the meantime, you'll likely have a waiting list of clients within three months of launching this physician-networking campaign using the three simple documents that I've given in this chapter. My final word of advice is this: the medical community loves three things:
- *Research-based practice:* Supply your patient/clients and your physicians with research-based nutrition and fitness articles. The Exercise is Medicine website is a great place to start.
- *Paper trails*: Keep a strict record of all workouts, patient/client data, and physician-interaction data.
- *Professionalism*: Follow the rules and HIPPA requirements. Don't share sensitive patient/client information with anyone except the physician.

Now get out there and practice exercise as medicine!

3

Online Training

You've heard of online personal training, but how does it work in practice? In this chapter, you'll learn how to host and build your website, advertise your online services, optimize client interactions, generate client testimonials, find free document-swapping tools for sharing files with your clients, upload photo and video, chat and talk to your clients live for no charge, and set up free FAQ and forums sections for your websites. You'll also learn the two top tips for launching you into an extremely high ranking position on a Google search.

Why You Need an Online
Personal-Training Presence

Picture your gym, health club, or studio. Imagine you've posted a sandwich-board style advertisement on the outside sidewalk. It boasts your expertise, knowledge, and guaranteed health, fitness, or weight loss results. Every day, perhaps 200 to 300 individuals walk past this sign and perhaps two percent actually pay attention and pop in to ask a few questions—that's four to six people.

Now, imagine that you had access to a multiplier. You can suddenly swell that 200 to 300 number a thousand fold. So now two to three million individuals walk past your sandwich board. Two percent still have a bit of interest and inquire about your services, but now that is 4000 to 6000 people, and you immediately have a client wait list.

If you know how to play your online-training card, this scenario can be a reality. Your local client base is finite. But in just one physically-unreachable area, (for example, England), millions of potential clients exist who can access your virtual expertise, if it is there to offer.

I've engaged in frequent paid live e-mail and phone consultations with clients from every corner of the globe, written weekly swim routines for open-water swimmers from Germany, coached Italian triathletes online with resistance-training photos and video, and written simple and effective weight-loss programs for citizens from nearly every state in America.

Perhaps you've heard that online training doesn't pay as much "per client." But I can perform four 20-minute Skype™ (www.skype.com) online chats for $60 per chat over the course of a single hour—*that's $240 per hour to sit in my pajamas, drink a smoothie, and type*. Rarely are your services offered on an hour-by-hour basis when you're training online, so you can squeeze quite a bit more work into the day (and you can do it in your pajamas). I now train a maximum of four to five "live" clients per day. Everything else is online. And the online work is much higher paying and much lower stress.

One other very important perk of maintaining an online training presence exists. Over the past year, I've had eight clients pack up and move away to new jobs, new lives, new towns, or new states. But they have the same personal trainer. That's right! Why should your clients ever quit training with you if they have complete online access to your knowledge and expertise? I simply tell my clients that I have a simple process to migrate them seamlessly into an online-training program that allows them to continue to see fabulous results every day. People love it, because they don't have to "cut the ties" with their trainer. Many clients still hire trainers in the cities that they move to, but continue to pay me to help design their program and interact with their new trainer.

The same can be said for clients who travel frequently. Why should they miss sessions when you can still receive your monthly paycheck and provide them with training or nutrition advice while they're on the road? No matter how you look at it, online training will improve your income—period—if you know what you're doing.

Establishing an Online Presence

First, you must find a host for your domain name. Your domain name can be whichever you choose. Usually, a combination of your name and the word fitness, wellness, or exercise works quite well (for example, www.bengreenfieldfitness.com). A host is an online company that you pay to host your domain name, meaning that you have full rights and access to modifying that domain. *The domain is your piece of virtual real estate, and the host ensures that it stays that way.* Typical hosting fees range from $5 to $10 per month, depending on the length of your hosting contract (usually one to two years), and the "goodies" that a host might throw in, like free website design or a huge amount of storage space for online photos and videos, etc.

I've used several different hosts in the past. Usually, the least expensive hosts have more than enough free e-mail addresses, web space, website templates, and special scripts like blogs and statistics. These add-ons have become so commonplace that it doesn't make sense to pay exorbitant web-hosting fees to what is usually your local friendly computer service, who simply can't compete with the larger online entities.

Traditionally, my favorite hosts have been either www.bluehost.com or www.godaddy.com. Bluehost not only has fantastic 24-7 tech support, but once you've purchased your domain name and hosting service, you have access to easy-to-install website features like online FAQ sections, forums for client interaction, special discounts on web design, and search engine submission.

GoDaddy.com® has many similar features, but in my experience, has a slightly less user-friendly control panel interface for your website. The nice part about www.godaddy.com is that when you go to search for available domain names, they suggest a huge range of other creative options if your desired name isn't available. For instance, if I type in bengreenfieldfitness.com, it may not be available, but bengreenfieldfitness.net, bgfit.us or fitnessbengreenfield.com may be alternatives. Now you have your domain name. It's a piece of blank real estate, so what next?

Building Your Website

In the past, I've personally done full graphic design and coding for 12 of my own websites. I've also had local community graphic web designers create two additional websites. But now, I outsource all this time-consuming work to Pakistan, India, or some other very inexpensive technology sector based geographical area. I talk comprehensively about this type of outsourcing in Chapter 5.

So, what methods have I used to create my websites? As mentioned previously, your hosting service will typically come complete with free web templates, which means that you can download the template to your computer, or you can use an online editing program that is usually available on your web host, and most of the work is done for you. The colors, backgrounds, and organization are already present, and you just drag and drop your desired pictures and text, which can be a very effective and quick way to design your website.

On the flipside, the website will have a very generic feel, and you have extremely limited control over the basic website design and organization. These type of sites have no "wow" factor, but if you're on a time crunch, have a limited budget, or just want to get started, it may be the way to go.

If you use an online website design tool, typically from your hosting service, you'll finish a web page on your website, then just press "publish" or "save," and it appears when people type your domain name (aka URL) into their computer's web browser.

If you use your own website design software, based from your computer, you typically have to create the website on your computer, then send it electronically (called FTP) to your hosting service, which typically provides pretty good instructions in the help section on how to use various web-design software to create and upload your site.

My favorite computer based software is Adobe® GoLive®, but if you go to www.download.com or www.tucows.com, you can download any number of free website design-software packages.

My Five Killer Tips for Your Website Design

- Keep it simple and clean. Include lots of "white space" so your readers don't become confused with 18 different training advertisements, fitness pop-ups, and sounds or music when they first visit your page.

- Use photos effectively. Try to include your face or body if possible, to build a trust relationship with your potential online clients and show that you are indeed fit.

- Use a simple navigation menu without too many buttons. A simple "home," "services," "about us," and "contact us" will suffice for a basic online personal-training page.

- Include space for publishing your latest breaking articles *on your home page*. This factor is very important for search-engine optimization, which I present later in this chapter.

- Include space for *publishing client testimonials* on a side bar or featured space on your home page. I designed an e-mail that I send out to each successful client after they've reached a milestone goal and have enough dopamine and endorphins rumbling through their system to give me a fantastic testimonial. Figure 3-1 is a letter that I send out to collect testimonials.

Dear _____,

The people I coach and train are my main focus in life. When you reach your goals, I feel I've contributed to your life in a unique way, and somehow contributed my knowledge to help you achieve something special and meaningful.

    I'm in the process of updating my website, specifically the online fitness and nutritional-training services. I really want people to know how I can help them achieve their desires.

    Here is where you come in. If you're interested, I'm looking for testimonials. Just a brief sentence or paragraph about how I've helped you identify objectives, reach your goals, or simply supplied you with a nudge in the right direction.

    If I use your testimonial on my website or in a brochure, I would just write your first name, or simply your initials if you'd prefer. All you really have to do is shoot your testimonial to me via e-mail.

    Thanks for considering, and remember to train and eat smart!

Cheers,
Ben

Figure 3-1

What else do you need to think about when designing your website?

- For online merchant capabilities, you'll need a shopping cart and credit card processing capabilities. Shopping-cart software will include clear instructions and support on how to integrate the shopping cart into your existing site. If you want a range of other options, such as newsletters, affiliate marketing, and advanced statistical tracking, use a site like www.1shoppingcart.com. Otherwise, you can actually use PayPal® (www.paypal.com) or Google Checkout®. (checkout.google.com) for absolutely free. These sites allow you to create simple purchase buttons that you can easily add to your websites.

- When you create your shopping cart, think about the concepts discussed in Chapter 1. Don't set your cart up so that a client purchases a single week or month of online training. The purchase button should actually be a "subscribe" button that is set up as a recurring payment. In Google, www.paypal.com, or www.1ShoppingCart.com, you can include options for your client to select the time length of the subscription. If you include a set -up fee for beginning online personal training, it will encourage clients to sign up for a longer time period of training.

Advertising Your Online Presence

You'll need to propagate your website among the hundreds of online search engines that exist on the web. Don't get caught up in this process. Once again, your hosting service can come to the rescue and typically provide very simple online search-engine submitting tools that will send your pages information to Google, Yahoo!®, HotBot®, and a host of other search engines.

Rather than wasting time with your search-engine submission process, use the suggested automatic submitting feature, then focus instead on making sure that search engines recognize rich content when they crawl across your site looking for keywords. Two important things exist to bear in mind when optimizing your search engine presence:

- *Include rich content on your home page*: The content should be typically in the form of fitness or nutrition articles that you have written. When a search engine comes across your website, it analyzes the type of website you have based on your text, and if no personal training related text on your site exists, the search engine is far less likely to put you at the top of the search results. For this reason, every time I write an article or a newsletter, I make sure it ends up somewhere on my website, thus presenting a search engine with that many more keywords to recognize.

- *Include "meta tags":* This tag is simply a line of code that lies in the background of your web page. It speaks very clearly to a search engine to explain the content of your website. A number of different websites have free meta tag creation tools. One example is www.orangesubmit.com. You simply type in your desired keywords (such as online personal training, diet and fitness consulting, free e-mail weight loss tips, etc.) and the tool generates a line of code that you then copy and paste into the code of your website.

However, in my opinion, an even more highly effective way to enhance your online presence is via article submission. If you type in any number of keywords to Google, such as "boost my metabolism," "healthy holiday eating," or "what exercise machine burns the most calories," you'll come across my name. As a matter of fact, I'm all over the web just about anywhere you search for diet and fitness information, and the majority of my online clients find me and hire me because they read one of my articles that is not on my website, but on a website like www.ezinearticles.com.

By submitting your articles to online article-submission websites such as E-Zine, and including a link or referral to your website in those articles, you will vastly improve your web presence. Part of the popularity contest on the web involves reciprocal linking, which basically means the number of hits you receive from a search engine is often dependent on the number of websites that actually feature your name or website.

Many websites exist that will not only host your articles for free but also distribute these articles to a range of other article-hosting websites. You simply include your article text, a bio, and a bit of personal information, and voila! Suddenly your article is all over the web, and you're the recognized expert on the topic. *Clients love to work with a published author, and usually don't care whether that publishing takes place on the Internet or in a paper book.*

Training Online

Now that you've built your website and advertised your services via search engine submission and online-article submission, you now must figure out how to actually train these clients. What services will you offer? How will you deliver those services?

I use two different methods to offer features to potential clients on my website. For the triathletes that I coach, I utilize an online coaching software called Peaksware, at www.trainingpeaks.com. This software enables me to advertise my services as *a top triathlon coach available to anyone, anywhere in the world* and allows me to do the following:

- *Design a complete annual training and racing plan based on each athlete's unique schedule, personal profile, skill level, limitations, and racing history*: The training plan is designed using online software, and is based on a comprehensive questionnaire that I send to each athlete when they inquire about training.

- *Allow detailed daily workout instructions to be automatically e-mailed to my clients*: Daily e-mails deliver the workouts each night, so each client can look ahead and see what the next week's workout will bring. They can even export their workouts to Outlook® calendars or PDAs to keep everything in one place. Full training log capability is also included, with graphing capabilities for miles logged, time spent at different heart-rate intensities, etc.

- *Track daily nutrition* and graph calories in versus calories out, macronutrient consumption, and other key diet variables. A complete menu planning suite is also available.

- *Download workout data* from client's PDA's, cyclocomputers, heart rate monitor, GPS or wattage software.

Training Peaks charges a monthly fee per each "premium" client that you coach online, which is pretty low overhead compared to a personal-training studio. They also offer an unlimited basic client option, which is completely free. You'll receive a line of script that you can copy and paste into your website HTML that gives a member username and password log-in window for your clients.

A nice feature is that website visitors will see the special area to which only members have access, and they will want access to that area. It's a great piece of marketing and can be a valuable component of your website's home page.

I use this software for my personal training clients, because I've discovered that it allows me to quickly write exercise and nutrition plans, design monthly programs, incorporate videos and photos, and copy and paste workouts between clients. Endurance athlete training is far more advanced, due to the training volume, necessity to peak properly for competition, and sharing of electronic GPS, heart rate, and power information. Therefore, I train many of these clients with the software's "premium" feature. But when people just want to lose weight, eat healthy, or get fit, I've found that a much simpler approach actually encourages more adherence to the program and is easier on both you and the client, so these clients are trained using the free "basic" feature.

In addition to online-training software, you can easily bootstrap your online training by beginning with something even less complicated. Using simple workout and meal plan templates that I've created in Microsoft® Word, I simply e-mail my general fitness/nutrition clients whichever documents that I need to share with them. For larger files that are not conducive to e-mail, I use two different document-sharing services. The first one is www.sendspace.com, which allows me to upload large photo and video collections, create a temporary link, and then send my client to that link to download the information. The second one is a free document-sharing service by www.google.com. Just go to Google and type in "google documents."

It is very easy in Microsoft Word to include links to photos and videos that you've already uploaded to your server, and are hosted at the same place as your domain name. I can create a directory online called "multimedia," for instance, and drag and drop any number of exercise photos and videos to this folder. Then, when my clients click on the name of the workout or exercise in the Word document, they are automatically directed to this content. Figure 3-2 is a sample workout plan I generated for clients. To include links to exercise photos and videos, I can simply select any exercise and go to "insert," then "hyperlink" in Word.

The same can be done with meal plans. Do you have a favorite recipe, nutrition website, or online calorie-tracking software? You can simply include links to these features in your client's meal plan. Figure 3-3 is a sample meal plan I created for a vegetarian triathlete.

Each meal includes a link to recipes from www.whfoods.com, one of my favorite nutrition-based websites. If you wanted to utilize more comprehensive online software that includes diet and calorie logging, workout logging, and fitness tracking, you can do it, but I've simply found that most clients don't even utilize these features, and it's more simple for us to just share files back and forth electronically. Remember, *less complication means more adherence*, and a lower "drop-out" rate for your trainees.

For log-keeping, I will typically send my clients a log similar to that in Figure 3-4, along with a sample log that I have already pre-populated with answers so that they can understand what type of information I need to see. At the end of this chapter, I include another log-keeping feature that I frequently utilize in the form of live chats and phone calls.

It is important to remember that once you've created a workout template for a specific client demographic, you can literally sell the actual workout series rather than selling your services. For example, I have one eight-week workout series called "The V-Body," which is available from my website for purchase and instant download. In the shopping cart, the product description reads, "An eight-week, four to six times per day resistance-training program that creates broad, cut shoulders, a razor-thin waistline, and

Mon	Tue	Wed	Thu	Fri	Sat/Sun
Workout 1	1. Cardio Intervals 1 2. Tue Metabolism Boosters	Workout 2	1. Cardio Intervals 2 2. Thu Metabolism Boosters	Workout 3	Attempt to log at least two hours easy cardio (walking, hiking, biking, etc.). On both days, complete at least three sets of 15 Rocket push-ups
Workout 4	1. Cardio Intervals 1 2. Tue Metabolism Boosters	Workout 1	1. Cardio Intervals 2 2. Thu Metabolism Boosters	Workout 2	On both days, complete three times through the following: • two minutes running, bicycling or stair-climbing • 15 Corkscrew push-ups • 15 Spiderman lunges per leg
Workout 3	1. Cardio Intervals 1 2. Tue Metabolism Boosters	Workout 4	1. Cardio Intervals 2 2. Thu Metabolism Boosters	Workout 1	On both days, complete at least three sets of 15 Rocket push-ups
Workout 2	1. Cardio Intervals 1 2. Tue Metabolism Boosters	Workout 3	1. Cardio Intervals 2 2. Thu Metabolism Boosters	Workout 4	On both days, complete three times through the following: • two minutes running, bicycling or stair-climbing • 15 Corkscrew push-ups • 15 Spiderman lunges per leg

Tuesday's Metabolism Booster—complete three to four times at some point during the day, preferably morning	Thursday's Metabolism Booster—complete three to four times at some point during the day, preferably morning
21 push jacks	14 lunge jumps per side
14 narrow grip push-ups	14 push-ups
14 six-inch crunches	21 mountain climbers to each side
21 body-weight squats	14 side planks to each side
14 pelvic lifts	21 kick-outs per side

Figure 3-2

Workout 1	Workout 2	Workout 3	Workout4
Warm-up with 10 minutes cardio of your choice.	Warm-up with 10 minutes cardio of your choice.	Warm-up with 10 minutes cardio of your choice.	Warm-up with 10 minutes cardio of your choice.
One set of 10 reps of each of the following, with minimal rest: Complete entire circuit four times through.	Complete the following four times, with minimal rest:	One set of 12 reps (or 12 reps per side) of each of the following, with minimal rest: Complete entire circuit three times through.	Complete six rounds of the following, with minimal rest:
Bent Row Weight: _____	20 reps medicine ball throw against the wall (from a deep squat)	Cable chest press Weight: _____	Seven reps one-arm dumbbell clean and press
Flat dumbbell chest press Weight: _____	25 reps sumo style deadlift (wide stance, narrow grip)	Deadlift Weight: _____	30 seconds running, cycling, or jump rope at 100%
Romanian deadlift Weight: _____	30 reps jumps onto bench (bench at least knee height)	Lateral lunge, curl & press Weight: _____	7 super-slow push-ups
Dumbbell walking lunges (10 reps/side) Weight: _____	35 reps push press (use barbell)	One-arm sips Weight: _____	14 mountain climbers
Hanging leg raise (hang from pull-up bar or use stirrups)	90 seconds maximum effort rowing machine	Little bigs Weight: _____	14 assisted pull-ups
Finish with five-minute cardio cool-down.		Cable kickbacks Weight: _____	30 seconds running, cycling, or jump rope at 100%
		Finish with five-minute cardio cool-down.	

Figure 3-2 (cont.)

Divide recipes by four for single-serving size

Breakfast & AM Snack

- Breakfast bagel
- Ginger yogurt with fruit
- Granola with fresh fruit
- Grapefruit sunrise
- Hot polenta breakfast with dried fruit compote (non-dairy)
- Italian tofu frittata
- Morning power smoothie
- Mushroom, tomato, basil frittata
- Perfect oatmeal
- Poached eggs over collard greens & shiitake mushrooms
- Poached eggs over sauteed greens
- Poached eggs over spinach & mushrooms
- Poached huevos rancheros
- Summer frittata
- Swiss breakfast
- Tropical breakfast risotto
- Tropical energy smoothie

Lunch (Salads or Soups)

Salads

- 10-minute fruit & cheese salad
- 15-minute black bean salad
- 15-minute Greek garbanzo bean salad
- Healthy Caesar salad
- Marinated bean salad
- Mediterranean pasta salad

Soups

- Five-spice onion soup
- Golden squash soup
- Miso soup
- Red kidney-bean soup with lime yogurt
- Shiitake mushroom seaweed soup
- Spicy cabbage soup
- Spicy posole soup
- Zesty Mexican soup

Afternoon Snack

- One handful snack mix
- Five to six slices celery with one tablespoon almond butter + one piece fruit
- Half sliced avocado with half red or green pepper, sliced. If prior to or after a workout, serve on a whole grain cracker or slice of bread + one piece fruit.
- Snack vegetables: one large handful sugar-snap peas, green beans, sliced peppers, olives or celery + one small handful walnuts or almonds
- Bar: BumbleBar, Biobar, or Larabar®
- Smoothie: choose one from list

Dinner (one entrée + one side salad *and* one side vegetable)

Entrées

- 15-minute asparagus, tofu stir-fry
- Black bean burrito, Indian style
- Black-bean chili
- Braised kidney beans & sweet potato
- Curried lentils
- Curried mustard greens & garbanzo beans with sweet potatoes
- Miso stir-fry
- Moroccan eggplant with garbanzo beans
- Polenta, onion, and gorgonzola pizza
- Spicy stir-fried tofu
- Vegetarian stir-fry

Side Salad/Dressings

- Chinese cabbage salad
- Creamy romaine salad (non-dairy)
- Cucumber & seaweed salad
- Fig, walnut, arugula salad
- Fresh minted garbanzo salad
- Grapefruit & arugula salad
- Great antipasti salad

Figure 3-3

- Lotza flavor marinated-vegetable salad
- Minted garbanzo-bean salad
- Romaine & avocado salad
- Tomato & dandelion salad

Side Vegetables

- Asian mushroom sauté
- Baked potato with rosemary & mushroom sauce
- Calabacitas—Mexican-flavored vegetable side dish
- Cranberry sauce
- Healthy mashed sweet potatoes (non-dairy)
- Marinated beets
- Mediterranean collard greens
- Mediterranean kale
- Mediterranean spinach
- Mediterranean Swiss chard
- Minted carrots with pumpkin seeds
- Pureed Navy beans
- Pureed sweet peas
- Sautéed greens
- Seaweed rice
- Steamed Mexican corn on the cob
- Steamed vegetable medley
- Wild rice pilaf

Snack 3 (during workout of one+ hour in duration—250 calories/hr)

- Bar: BumbleBar, Biobar, or Larabar—one/hr
- Energy drink: 200-250 calories/hr (no soy!)
- Energy gel: two to three/hr (pref honey, brown rice, syrup, or glucose base)
- Fruit: Two small or one medium-large/hr
- Berries: Two handfuls/hr
- Sweet potato: Two small or one medium-large/hr

Snack 4 (Post-workout within 20 minutes)

- One cup smoothie: choose one from list
- One handful snack mix: choose one from list
- Sweet potato: two small or one medium-large with one tablespoon almond butter
- Bar: BumbleBar, Biobar or Larabar
- Oatmeal: 100 calories + one egg
- Fruit: One piece fresh and raw with One handful almonds or walnuts
- Bread + chicken: One slice Ezekiel bread with two to four oz. chicken breast
- Quinoa: 150 to 200 calories
- Recoverite: One serving

Figure 3-3 (cont.)

Combined Diet and Exercise Log			
Diet Log			**Exercise Description**
Food description: Be as specific as possible, including brands when applicable. Include water and supplements.	**Time of day:**	**Energy and hunger:** Include notes about how your body felt. Include wake time and bedtime.	**Strength/cardio/other:** Include workout description, heart-rate data, or approximate intensity, sets, reps, time of day, and length.

Figure 3-4

bulging quads. Get your V-Body today." *The client presses purchase, the workout downloads automatically to their computer, and I do...nothing (aside from the initial two hours of work I spent designing the program).* If sales seem to drop off, I can send out a marketing newsletter that advertises, for example, a complimentary e-mail consultation with the purchase of any program.

Multimedia

Of course, one of the key missing variables in virtual personal training is your lack of ability to demonstrate exercises to your clients. This factor is the missing feature that most clients will complain about, unless you have some way to show them what a "rocket push-up" or "Hindu squat" is.

With the advent of websites like YouTube, it is very easy for your search for an exercise, and as long as you're using exercises with tradition names like "squat" or "dumbbell bench press," a savvy web trainee will be videos of any exercise by utilizing search engines and online-video webs recommend this approach if you just need to launch your online-training service don't have time to shoot and upload your own photos and videos. However, th method is inconvenient for your client and will remove the custom feel of your training, thus ultimately decreasing the fees that you can charge.

For time management, I highly recommend the *batching* approach to exercise photo and video creation, which means that you write down a large number of exercises, like 25 to 50, and record them all at once. This method will be quicker than setting up your equipment to shoot just a few exercises in a day. Nowadays, just about any digital camera or video recorder will allow for seamless data uploading to a laptop or PC. I use a handheld Sony® HD camcorder for videos and a Nikon® CoolPix® for photos.

You'll need an assistant to record the exercises that you demonstrate. Give them a list of the exercises you're going to demonstrate. To save time when you edit your video clips, make sure your assistant writes down on this list the time (i.e., 8:12:11) on the video when you start and stop an exercise. For photos, your assistant should just record the number of the photo next to the actual exercise on the list. Usually, I just freeze frame my videos to harvest any exercise photos that I need, but if you're not shooting any video, this approach may be the most appropriate.

Ensure that you have a clear background. You'd be surprised at how posters, neon lights, people, and exercise machines can muddy up an exercise demonstration. Do not wear loose fitting clothing, as it will appear unprofessional in the video and viewers may have a difficult time seeing key joints.

Once you've shot your video, you can use a USB cable or Firewire cable attached from the camera to a port on your computer to upload video. Most cameras come with a driver that you need to install on your computer, which will also include any necessary software to help your computer recognize the hardware. Often the same software can be used to edit your multimedia.

On my Macintosh®, I use iMovie®HD for video editing. It is very similar to the PC version of *Windows Movie Maker*. Both of these programs are simple to use, and have capabilities to take a workout video that you upload and automatically create clips for each exercise. You can then add text, music, titles, credits, and any other dress-up features that you choose. Another program, called *Dartfish®*, is highly effective for editing and biomechanically analyzing video, but is, in my opinion, time-consuming and a poor investment for online training. I use it in my biomechanics lab for running gait analyses and bicycle fits, but like to use simpler software for online-video editing.

a, you can export, upload, and FTP to your server host. slash in your URL, and the name of your video or r example, let's say I want to share a multimedia v and throw exercise with my clients. I'll upload it to a gleLegRowThrow.mov," "SingleLegRowThrow.avi," or nding on the file format that I exported the video with. type pacificfit.net/trivideos/SingleLegRowThrow.mov of the single leg row and throw. I can then copy and at I've written, or can simply e-mail the link to a client.

Ensure that your multimedia is formatted to a low enough quality that it will upload quickly to your client's computer. *When simply viewing and learning exercises, people care far less about video or photo quality compared to the speed of downloading.* The best format for photos is a .gif and the best format for videos is a .wmv. I've universally had very little trouble with both these formats. The beauty of multimedia creation and online uploading is that once you've created it, you never have to do it again, it's always there at that same URL, and you can use it for future clients, or more importantly, information product creation, which I discuss in Chapter 9.

Live Consulting

If you're like many personal trainers, you still desire some type of live interaction with your virtual clients. Simply hearing your voice or seeing a live chat can help a client remember that you are indeed a real person, and they're paying to utilize the services of a true expert, not a random computer that generates daily workouts or meal plans.

Initially, I used phone calls for this purpose, typically scheduling them on the weekends to save on cell-phone bills. About three to four days prior to their "check-in" call, I would send clients an e-mail reminding them of the day and time. I would also batch these calls, so that I could contact six clients over the course of an hour. It is very important that your reminder e-mail includes the scheduled time length of the phone call. Ten minutes will suffice for a monthly check-up. These ten minutes out of each month for your online clients will keep them renewing their online subscription month-after-month, because it is a special personal touch that people truly appreciate.

Today, I am more prone to use the free live chat and national/international computer-based communication service from www.skype.com. You simply download the free software to your computer, create a username, and you are automatically accessible to your clients for live chat and audio whenever you log in to Skype. Your clients will also need to have Skype downloaded on their computer, but it is very easy to do.

In addition to live interaction with existing clients, you'll be able to use e-mail, Skype, and the phone to include consulting as part of your listed services. This factor can be a highly profitable aspect of your online-training business.

E-mail Consulting

A client can go to my website and pay for a single e-mail consultation. Upon receiving notice of this purchase from my online shopping cart, an autoresponder sends an e-mail back to the client with the following message:

> "Congratulations! You now have access to the nation's leading expert on exercise, nutrition, and wellness. Your e-mail consultation with Ben Greenfield allows you to get answers to your most pressing fitness, diet, or health questions.
>
> Ben's personal e-mail address is ben@bengreenfieldfitness.com. Please limit your e-mail inquiry to no more than 500 words.
>
> Upon receiving your question(s) via e-mail, Ben will respond with a detailed response within 48 hours. Thank you!"

I've never spent more than 15 minutes responding in an e-mail consultation, and the client is always satisfied.

Phone Consulting

Upon receiving notice of a phone consultation purchase from my online shopping cart, an autoresponder sends an e-mail back to the client with the following message:

> "Congratulations! You now have access to the nation's leading expert on exercise, nutrition, and wellness. Your phone consultation with Ben Greenfield allows you to get answers to your most pressing fitness, diet, or health questions.
>
> Please respond to this e-mail with a list of the best weekday and weekend times during which you have a 20- to 30-minute time availability and the best phone number to call you at during these times. You will then be contacted via e-mail within 48 hours to schedule your phone consultation. Thank you!"

Before I purchased an "unlimited minutes" cell-phone plan, I would usually attempt to schedule phone consultations on the weekend to save money on cell phone bills.

Live Online Chat

Upon receiving notice of a live-chat purchase from my online shopping cart, an autoresponder sends an e-mail back to the client with the following message:

> "Congratulations! You now have access to the nation's leading expert on exercise, nutrition, and wellness. Your live chat with Ben Greenfield allows you to get answers to your most pressing fitness, diet, or health questions.
>
> Please go to www.skype.com to download the free software that will allow you to chat live with Ben Greenfield. Upon activating the software on your computer, please respond to this e-mail with your Skype username. You will then be contacted via e-mail within 48 hours to schedule your live chat. Thank you!"

I usually limit live chats to no longer than 20 minutes. What you charge for these services is up to you. You decide how much you're worth—you're in control. You'd be surprised at what people will pay.

Interaction

People love interaction, and will be more likely to be repeat visitors to your website if a constantly modified information source exists that draws them in, which is the same reason people repeatedly visit or subscribe to blogs and to online newsletters. (Refer to Chapter 4 for more information about these tools.)

A great way for you to constantly modify the information on your website *without* actually spending hours of your own time is to simply *have your clients and website visitors submit the content*, which can be accomplished via two methods: online FAQs and Forums. Most hosting services include a feature to activate either of these functions in your website, and you can link to this section directly from the homepage.

FAQs

Over the course of many years of online-personal training, I've received just about every fitness and diet question you can imagine and I've responded to the majority of them. Many of the questions and many of the responses are identical. It wouldn't make sense for me to write the same book three or four times, and eventually I realized that it didn't make sense for me to respond to the same questions over and over again, which is where an online FAQ section can come in handy. This section is available to my paying clients, and allows them to log in to an FAQ section where they can view questions that other clients have previously asked, as well as my responses to those questions. Once you've had your FAQ section up and running for several months, you'll notice that your "question-answering" workload diminishes significantly. Once a week, I'll visit the online FAQ and respond to the questions that my clients have posted. My responses are immediately available for viewing. If you want to take your FAQ public, you can, but I prefer to include it as a bonus feature for my paying clients.

Forums

A forum is similar to an FAQ, in that it is modifiable by both you and your registered website visitors. You can use a forum to turn a section of your website into a type of social interaction page. By including topics such as "My Favorite Workout," "Recipes," and "Metabolism Boosting Tips," you'll allow your website visitors to log in and contribute their own content. Similar to the FAQ page, each week you can log in and comment on the forum activity. You'll find that this activity turns you into a bit of a mini-celeb on your own website forum—the guru who drops in every now and then to moderate the conversation.

When you visit other forums outside your webpage, you can automatically improve the number of your own website hits by including a link to your website underneath your signature on your forum user bio, which you must create when you register for a forum. About 15% of my website hits come from people reading a post that I've left at a forum like www.slowtwitch.com, and then clicking through to my website, which appears under my username.

A useful tip that I personally utilize is to create a reminder on your phone, PDA, or computer to log in to a select number of these type of forums and comment on a weekly basis. Out of sight is out of mind, but by having a constant reminder, you are far more likely to "socially network" on forums.

FAQs and forums merely scratch the surface of your ability to engage in rich interaction with your online client and fan base. Chapter 4 introduces you to Web 2.0, and the opportunity to virally market an enormous online-client base.

4

The New Web

This chapter will teach you how to turn yourself into an online celebrity and recognized expert in your niche market, using cutting-edge search-engine optimization tools like audio and video podcasting™, blogging, RSS, Google AdWords® and AdSense®, affiliate marketing, opt-in lists, e-newsletters, and add-on domains. Using techniques like viral-video marketing and keyword-driven online-ad campaigns, you'll learn exactly how to maximize your online presence, rise above the local and online-training competition, and reap enormous financial rewards using the latest technology. (*Note*: For updated information that accommodates the rapidly changing structure of the Internet, visit my blog www.trainfortopdollar.com, which provides a free newsletter with monthly updates on enhancing your web presence as a personal trainer.)

Web 2.0 Defined

Most trainers think of their online presence as a type of Yellow Pages advertisement. It tells readers what you do and what your specialty is, supplies your contact information, and perhaps includes some pictures or bold advertisements to grab the viewer's attention.

If you're slightly more advanced, like on my first few websites, you might have some special online submission forms for your clients and potential customers to send you health-history information or diet/exercise logs, a member's log-in area with a username and password, and maybe some exercise photo and video content. You might even have a FAQ and Forum section, as mentioned in Chapter 3. *But to truly take it to the next level, become a top-ranked search engine website, and drive yourself to the peak of Internet celebrity status, you must have some semblance of Web 2.0 capability*. Features on my website bengreenfieldfitness.com, for example, include the following:

- I have a weekly fitness podcast that I record in my home and then broadcast across the Internet. Thousands of people every week can automatically subscribe via iTunes® and download my podcast for free to their computer. During the podcast, I share free information that benefits the user, and then I plug anything I feel like plugging, including my books, DVDs, seminars, clinics, or training and coaching services. Every time I publish my podcast to the Internet, it includes a very clear title and description that allows any search engine to recognize my podcast as rich and useful content, thus increasing my visibility in search engines.

- I write a daily blog posting. This blog again offers free fitness, nutrition, or wellness advice, and can include links or references to any of my information, products, or services online. Every time I publish my blog, it appears on my home page. Thus, any search engine that crawls that page comes across constantly updated and relevant content, again improving my search-engine status and ranking. Any user can not only automatically subscribe to my blog, but can also comment on or rank the usefulness of my blog posting. The information flows two ways.

- I publish weekly exercise-video podcasts on my website. These videos are very similar to the audio podcasts, but instead of simply limited the videos to my website and iTunes subscription, I also upload them to YouTube with very clear titles and descriptions. I also send links to my videos to other blogs, MySpace® groups, Facebook® pages, and any other friends who publish similar content, thus increasing my reciprocal linking and again enhancing my search-engine presence and website credibility. This job of video content distribution is outsourced (refer to Chapter 5).

- I have a newsletter subscription button, in which someone can type in their name and e-mail address, and, in exchange, receive a subscription to my newsletter, which basically features one article by me, and then a bunch of click-through advertisements to my affiliates. Because of this subscription button, I have legal access to my marketing "list." The list includes thousands of consumers who are interested in the information or services that I provide.

- I have affiliate logos and links. Because I utilize affiliate click-through software, anytime that someone clicks a link for one of the featured fitness or nutrition-related supplement, book, or website, the software automatically tracks that click. Furthermore, the software will track if that person purchases a product on my affiliate's website and I receive a percentage of the sale.

- I have a Google AdSense program. This program enables text, image, and video advertisement content on my website, provided by Google and limited to the content that satisfies keywords which I've pre-approved. These ads generate revenue on a pay-per-click basis. This job of keyword creation is outsourced (refer to Chapter 5).

- I also have a Google AdWords program. This program is similar to Google AdSense, but instead of me receiving a paycheck when people click on the provided links, I pay Google a nominal fee anytime something clicks-through on an advertisement for any of my websites utilizing links that I've created using highly targeted and specific keywords. This job of ad creation is outsourced (refer to Chapter 5).

- Finally, I include links to all my books and DVDs from a page at bengreenfieldfitness.com. Why not just sell the products directly from the website? Reciprocal linking! By creating separate websites for each of my products, I simply enhance my web presence and "spread the empire" a bit farther across the Internet globe.

All of the aforementioned tools are part of my Web 2.0 website. What is Web 2.0 exactly? Several definitions exist. The following explains the basic concept:

- Users of your website can contribute content to your website to create a true network society effect.

- You can push information to your clients, visitors, users, and fans in a very automated and convenient fashion. Information flows two ways. It takes the concept of the FAQ and the forum discussed in Chapter 3 to a whole new level.

- Software applications used to enhance Web 2.0 websites are often "open-ended" and can be modified by the software users themselves, thus creating constantly evolving and usually free web applications.

Samples of Web 2.0-esque websites include: eBay®, Craigslist®, Wikipedia®, Delicious, Skype, Flickr®, Google Docs, Yahoo! Local, MapQuest®, and any website that combines technologies, such as weblogs (blogs), wikis, podcasts, RSS feeds, and social networking capabilities with constantly evolving web applications.

The type of software that is used in a Web 2.0-style website is usually located on your server, and not on your computer. You can typically find "plug-ins" and "extensions" for your Web 2.0 software, free for downloading from other websites. The content of the website is syndicated, meaning that new "news" is always showing up on your pages. Messaging protocols like blogs and comments abound. Social networking, such as links from your blog or podcast to sites like YouTube, Facebook, and MySpace are common, thus vastly improving your site's visibility.

Web 2.0 provides for a rich, interactive experience between you and the greater web community. This chapter is designed to give you a basic overview of some of the practical ways that you can use Web 2.0 to enhance your training business and popularity.

RSS

On a Web 2.0-capable website, people can upload their content to your website and download your content to their computer, usually automatically. The content downloading is possible via a type of subscription service called RSS, which stands for really simple syndication. You may recognize RSS capable websites because of the universally recognizable square orange "soundwave" RSS logo that typically appears somewhere on the page.

Whenever you have frequently updated content on your website, which is part of the definition of a Web 2.0 website, you must have RSS feed capabilities in order for your users to automatically be alerted of and have access to that content. This is called a web feed, or channel. RSS makes it possible for people to stay alerted of your website content in an automated manner.

People who download your content will automatically have to have special software called "RSS reader," "feed reader," or "aggregator," I recommend FeedDemon® at www.feeddemon.com for the PC and NewsGator at http://www.newsgator.com for the Mac®. When your users click the RSS feed button on your website, this software automatically subscribes to your web feeds and downloads them on a daily, weekly, or monthly basis to the user's computer (depending on how frequently you update your website's Web 2.0 content). Therefore, whether you have a blog feeds, audio-podcast feeds, or video-podcast feeds, you must have RSS Feed capabilities for your users to be able to automatically access your feeds.

I highly recommend using a free blog-style web software called WordPress® to create your Web 2.0 website. WordPress is the Web 2.0-style platform I use to run bengreenfieldfitness.com. If you're using a web host like www.bluehost.com, then WordPress is easy to download with just one simple click. Just log in to your control panel and then click on Simple Scripts. You'll have access to WordPress automatically, for free.

WordPress is fully RSS capable, and from your WordPress administration interface, you'll find that you can easily add that little orange RSS button to any page on your blog, whether it be your actual blog, your podcasts, or your videos (of course, you should have a separate RSS feed for each). You can download free themes for WordPress, or pay for a theme template that has a design that you prefer. You can easily modify this theme, adding your own titles and menu navigation using the WordPress administration interface.

Thousands of plug-ins exist for WordPress . These plug-ins, which are easy to install and download, allow you to do things, such as have your uploaded podcasts automatically distributed to websites like www.feedburner.com, change your website's keywords meta-tags (refer to Chapter 3) based on the content that you've uploaded for that day, and allow users to "rank" your blog postings or videos.

A website called www.tubetorial.com reveals a huge number of useful tips and tricks that you can use for your WordPress -style blog. I highly recommend visiting the website and perusing the interactive-video presentations.

Once you have set up your feeds, you'll need to make sure that non web-savvy users understand exactly how to subscribe to a feed. The best way to ensure that y can explain the process clearly to your clients and customers is to make sure th know how to do it yourself.

So, let's try it out! The following is a step-by-step process that I highly recommend you try now:

- Download a feed reader to your computer. Popular feed readers include www.newsgator.com, which can automatically feed subscriptions into your e-mail box, but there are a ton of different options for RSS readers, including Microsoft Outlook plug-ins or plug-ins for browsers like Firefox® or Apple®'s newest Safari® browser, which also has an RSS reader. But the NewsGator® is a good free reader that is easy to use and allows you to track your feeds anytime, anywhere, from any browser, by just logging into your free NewsGator account online.
- Next, go to www.trainfortopdollar.com.
- Click on "blog."
- Right click on the RSS feed button (or control-click if you're on a Mac), and choose "copy link." An RSS feed button is typically a little square orange box, with what looks like a "speaker" wave inside it. At www.trainfortopdollar.com, it is about halfway down the page, just above the "Archives" section.
- Go to your NewsGator page and sign-in, then click on "Add Feeds."
- Click URL and Import.
- Choose edit, then paste from your browser menu into the text-input box.
- Then click "Add Feed."

That's it! *From this point, whenever you go to your NewsGator page, the latest tips and tricks from Train for Top Dollar website will appear in your browser window.*

There's no way you can keep track of all the different blogs you may want to read, so this method is a great way to subscribe to them for free. It's just like getting the newspaper delivered to your front door, rather than making a trip to the supermarket to buy it each morning.

Blog

A blog is just a short version of the term web log, and refers to a website that has regular entries of commentary, event descriptions, or any other frequently updated photos. "Blogging" is the verb used to describe what you're our blog.

our own free blog. Even if you don't want to pay for a web luehost.com to host a WordPress-style blog, you can easily ne-based software found at websites like www.blogger.com, r http://bengreenfieldtri.blogspot.com, for my triathlon race ogger™ allows me to add sidebar links, videos, photos, or any other rich content. Granted, it doesn't have the same amount of plug-ins or extensions as WordPress, but it's a great place to start if you haven't blogged before and want a simple, easy-to-use interface.

A daily blog post may take you 5 to 15 minutes, and will pay dividends. The following list describes how you can use a blog to enhance your personal-training business:

- *If you have information products like books, e-books, or DVDs, then be sure to constantly refer to these products in your blog postings*, even if it is just in one small sentence. For example, when reporting on a recent road trip, I referred to the fact that at every gas station stop, I performed 100 jumping jacks, and then explained that I harvested this fitness tip from my book, *100 Ways to Boost Your Metabolism*. Of course, I then included a link to the book's website in my blog posting. This way, you are providing people with useful information in your blog post while simultaneously using high-technology marketing to feature your products and services.

- *If you rely on your blog to enhance your face-to-face personal training services, then use client anecdotes and testimonials*, and don't be afraid to frequently ask your clients for simple e-mail quotes that you can use in the next day's blog posting. As soon as you start your blog, you'll find that many of your clients become frequent visitors and commentators, and they'll love to see their own quotes up in the spotlight. Try using the request for testimonials found in Chapter 3. Toss these anecdotes into random stories. For example, "Just the other day I was training a client and he/she commented that they 'had dropped two pant sizes'. This is, of course, the downside of rapidly melting away fat—having to buy a whole new wardrobe!"

- *Post a workout or recipe of the week*. You'll find that potential clients use this posting as a way to identify your fitness or nutrition style, and many of them will become frequent fans of your weekly special. Don't reveal how to insert the workout or recipe of the week into a "perfect" fitness or diet program, but instead advertise your services as a means of truly gaining the knowledge of how to "use the weekly special." CrossFit.com is a perfect example of a blog-style program that utilizes daily workouts, but also advertises memberships to local chapters and subscriptions to paid newsletters for real CrossFit® programs.

- *Tell everyone about your blog*. There's something addicting about reading other's blogs, and since people can subscribe to your blog via an RSS feed, you may find that some individuals read you as regularly as a newspaper, and hang on your every word. They then include links to your blog from their blog, and e-mail or forward your blog postings to friends, who then subscribe to your RSS feed. This is called viral marketing. It starts very small and spreads very quickly.

One last important tip on blogging: in your administrator interface, make sure you turn on the option for search engines to be able to access your blog and the option for anyone to comment on your blog postings. Otherwise, your posts will remain private, flow only one direction, and have much less impact.

Audio Podcast

A podcast is a digital media file that, similar to a blog posting, is syndicated using a feed-based service. When you blog, you're blogging, and when you podcast, you're podcasting.

Typically, when you create an audio or video file for a user-podcast subscription, you can also make it available on your website for immediate download. Often, you'll find that users subscribe to your podcast *after* downloading and listening to one of your audio files that you've made available for immediate download. That way, they "try," then they "buy."

In addition to a decent computer with two to three gigabytes of free hard drive space, a soundcard, at least 512 megabytes RAM, and a microphone input/headphone output, you're going to need some basic gear and software to get started in podcasting. I recommend the following:

- Headphones or headset: Pretty much any headphones that plug into your computer will work, but headsets are typically better, since the microphone and headphones are combined. I use the Altec Lansing AHS 302i.

- Microphone: If you go for the headphones and purchase a microphone separately, get something inexpensive and easy to use, like the Labtec 524, or any other decent microphone you can find at Radio Shack.

- Podcasting software: Most Macs automatically come with a decent podcasting-capable software called GarageBand®. I prefer to use the free Audacity® podcast software from www.audacity.com. It comes with a pretty decent help file to walk you through the recording and file-exporting process. Once you've created your audio file, it's easy to upload to your server, using the same FTP protocols discussed in Chapter 3.

OK, you have your gear. Now how do you start your podcast? Extemporaneous speaking is hard. Trying to throw together an impromptu show will leave you sounding uneducated and ill prepared. Instead create a show outline prior to recording. This process is especially useful, because after you've created your podcast, you can create show notes from your outline. You can then publish these show notes to the web as yet another form of search-engine-friendly content.

Organize your show content using whatever structure you're comfortable with, just as long as you have a rough schedule to follow as you record. If you plan on utilizing multimedia content, you can include cues for audio clips or music in your show notes. The following is a sample outline for one of my fitness podcasts:

- Intro theme song and welcome message:

"Welcome to the bengreenfieldfitness.com podcast, your weekly free audio exposure to cutting-edge fitness, diet, and wellness news. Whether you're an Ironman triathlete or just trying to shed a few pounds, we've got rich, healthy content from the nation's leading expert."

- Introduce myself and, if present, my co-host
- Song 1
- Announcements: fitness and nutrition news
  - ✓ High fructose corn syrup/glycemic index link
  - ✓ Dumbbell vs. barbell bench-press
  - ✓ ACSM Exercise as medicine initiative
- Introduce podcast topics
- Song 2
- Topic 1: Metabolic tip of the day
- Song 3
- Topic 2: How to measure resting metabolic rate
- Song 4
- Topic 3: Top calorie-burning exercise modes
- Song 5
- Closing song and closing message
    "That's today's podcast from bengreenfieldfitness.com. For more free advice, groundbreaking books, DVDs, and information products from Ben Greenfield, visit bengreenfieldfitness.com."

So, should you have a show co-host? *There is a reason that the most popular radio shows have two DJs.* Generally, your listeners will find it far more interesting to hear you argue with a co-host about your topics than to hear you spew information solo. Discussion is far more interesting than a lecture. If you're utilizing the free Skype software, your co-host doesn't even have to be in the same room as you. You can easily record your podcast via Skype with a co-host from a completely different geographical region.

If you record your podcast at home, make sure to find a quiet, private room and close the door. Alert your family or housemates that you are recording, pay attention to any outdoor distractions like lawnmowers or jackhammers, turn off fans or air conditioning in the room, and eliminate cell phones and alarms if possible.

If you record in a public place, make sure you talk as closely as you can without distortion, and do a test recording to make sure your surrounding environment isn't too distracting. Believe it or not, you can easily podcast while driving in your car, as long as you pay attention to the road. The following ideas are some tips on using a podcast to enhance your personal-training business:

- When you submit your RSS feed to iTunes, you're able to submit album artwork. If you've got a face for TV or a cut body, then use it on your album artwork. People will become familiar with your profile and establish a trust relationship. If you don't have album artwork, iTunes just assigns you a generic iTunes logo, which does not help you stand out from the pack, which you'll need to do if you truly want to *train for top dollar.*

- If you use WordPress , install the FeedBurner® plug-in as a free WordPress add-on. If you use Blogger or some other web blog format, or even just a "normal" static HTML website, then submit your podcast to www.feedburner.com. FeedBurner will automatically submit your podcast to iTunes when you publish. This will save you quite a bit of time.

- *Include frequently featured interviews.* Interview your clients, your massage therapist, your physician, your next door neighbor, and any other personality that will generate health discussion and make your podcast interesting. Similar to featuring a co-host, you will find it much simpler to create content when you're bouncing ideas, questions, or arguments off someone else.

- *Keep it simple.* Sure, the show outline in this chapter is somewhat comprehensive, but you can literally begin with a just a five-minute fitness tip-style podcast. Build it from there as you gather listeners and build a fan base.

- *Use Q&As.* Reveal in your podcast an e-mail address for your listeners to send their fitness or nutrition questions, then read and answer these questions on the air. This vastly enhances your user interaction, and ensures that you maintain relevant content.

- *Always be selling.* Remember, the podcast is ultimately about your bottom line. Don't let a single audio file escape without some mention of a personal-training membership special, book sale, new DVD product, or affiliate supplement.

- *Advertise.* Speaking of affiliates, you will find that as your podcast grows in popularity, you build a platform upon which to sell advertising to your affiliates. Supplement, nutrition, and fitness companies can pay any price you feel like naming to run an ad, or have you create an ad for them. By simply choosing a catchy background tune and having your spouse or significant other read a supplement advertisement in a catchy voice, you can automatically generate enough ad revenue to justify the minutes you spend creating your podcast.

Videos

Think of video feeds as just another form of blogging or podcasting. In the same way that you upload audio files for podcasts or text for blogs, you can upload video for RSS feeds to your Web 2.0-ized site. These videos can be actual interviews with you or another fitness professional, workout and exercise demonstrations, or excerpts from an exercise video or DVD that you've created.

Keep your videos brief. The most popular videos on YouTube do not typically exceed three minutes. People have a short attention span, and video takes up a large amount of web space and takes a longer time to download than audio or text files.

The following are some other tips for shooting your video:
- *Use close-up shots*: The closer you are to a subject, the less distraction in the background, and the easier it is for software to compress your video file. Keep your background plain and it will improve the way your main video subject appears.
- *Lighting*: If lighting has too much contrast or there is a bright light behind the object you're filming, it will again be difficult to compress a quality video file.
- *Audio*: Cut out any loud background noises and use an external microphone if you're filming from any farther away than three feet.
- *Limit camera movement*: Use a tripod and avoid excessive zooming and panning. This step can cause frame skipping when you compress the video.
- *Write big*: When you edit your video and add titles or credits, use large fonts, as they will grab more attention.

I've found that the best file format for quick uploading are a .wmv or .avi file. Quicktime.mov files are another popular format, but I've had more trouble with users downloading and experiencing problems with these files. YouTube specifically recommends MPEG4 (DivX, Xvid, SVQ3) format at 64k Mono MP3 audio and 30 frames per second, with a 4:3 aspect ratio. You can export one of these more reliable video files using any type of popular video creation software, such as Windows Movie Maker. Another procedure is *viral video marketing*, which is a simple technique that you can use to quickly spread your videos across the web and almost instantly skyrocket your search-engine rankings and sell thousands of books. Here's how to do viral-video marketing:

- *Record your video*. Use the tips from Chapter 3. Once you have your video edited and ready for the web, FTP it to your server, and then upload it to YouTube. You'll need a free YouTube account and username, which is easy to get. Use the following URL to read more tips on YouTube uploading and viral video: http://tinyurl.com/videoviralyoutube

- *Include a link to your website* in your YouTube video description. Also include a link to your website as a title in your video edit, and make sure that the title appears for several seconds after your video has ended so that the viewer has time to type the URL into their browser.

- *Use very specific keywords* and include a complete description of the video content in the YouTube description section. This is how a search engine will find your video.

- *Send a link to your YouTube video* to every MySpace, Facebook, or blog connection that you have. I get college interns to do this for me (refer to Chapter 5 for more details), because they're typically wired in to a large number of social networks. Think about the idea of six degrees of separation. If you have good content, your video will quickly make its way around the world. A useful website is http://www.tubemogul.com, which has the capability to actually send your video to multiple video-featuring websites.

- *Use your videos to sell*. If you are making an e-book with links to exercise videos, you should include the videos to be available as external links to high quality video hosted on your server (linked to from your e-book), but also make the videos available for free on YouTube. Sure, people can watch your video on YouTube without paying, but they really won't know how to utilize the exercises in a workout unless they purchase your e-book. Make sure you mention this fact in your video— you're tempting them.

For a perfect example of how I effectively used this viral video-marketing technique to sell scores of my book, *Top 12 Resistance Training Routines for Triathletes*, from www.thestrongtriathlete.com, in a span of about seven hours, just go to YouTube and search for videos by thestrongtriathlete. I've done it with other books and it works wonders for your marketing campaign.

Ad Campaigns

Three important and very powerful advertising tools exist that you can use to enhance your personal training web presence, your face-to-face sales with clients who are looking for a local personal trainer, and your automated income (AKA money that you make while you're asleep). Google AdSense is an advertisement program run by, of course, Google. You submit your website information to Google, enroll in the program, and enable text, image, and video advertisements to appear on your site. You receive a tiny paycheck anytime someone clicks on these ads. It doesn't matter whether they purchase anything from the click-through website, although Google is testing such a cost-per-action based service. Currently, I use higher quality, more targeted affiliate links for that method. AdSense is useful for delivering revenue to sites that may not have full advertising sales programs or affiliate programs in place, but you need to be careful.

I once ran a Google AdSense script (by copying and pasting the code that Google provided me onto the books section of my website), only to realize that I ended up with ads plastered across my books page that were selling books in direct competition to me. Sure, I might make a few bucks a day off these ads, but I might sell 10 fewer actual books! One way I use Google AdSense very effectively is on the newsletter archives section of my website, where I have hundreds of different fitness articles on various topics. By copying and pasting my Google AdSense script in the header section of each of these article webpages, Google will generate ads that reflect the keywords presented in that particular article. If I write a story on how to lose weight during travel, Google will run ads across the top of that page that sell plane tickets, rental cars, and elastic bands for portable exercise. This is one way to create highly targeted and demographic-specific advertisements that instantly change, depending on the page that a viewer clicks on in your website.

Google AdWords is just the opposite. You design the ads that will appear on other websites that are running Google AdSense ads. In this case, you supply Google with your ad information, the amount that you are willing to pay-per-click for the various keyword and ad combinations that you submit, and the Google search technology places your ad on relevant websites (i.e., fitness and nutrition websites, or perhaps if you're specific enough with your niche targets, bridal weight loss and exercise fuel for vegan websites). Since you're paying every time someone clicks on these ads, you should make sure that your ads are very specific, because you don't want to be forking over thousands of nickels and dimes for every John Doe who sees your website advertisement on "general fitness," click through to your website, and immediately realizes that it doesn't give him what he wanted, which was "how to get a six pack within two weeks using only a treadmill and two 10-pound dumbbells."

The following list is some tips for your Google AdWords campaign:

- *Be specific with your ad links*. If you're selling a nutritional supplement from one special section of your webpage, but your AdWords ad has the user click-through to the main section of your webpage, that's one more jump the user has to make to actually find the supplement once they get to your website. Skip that step and take them straight there.

- *Create separate and specific campaigns*. Don't just have one AdWords campaign for your general line of weight-loss supplements. Run a specific campaign for each specific product—one for the fat burner, one for the metabolism booster, one for the carbohydrate resister, etc. Have a separate list of keywords for each product or service and don't duplicate those keywords across each product.

- *Use geographical regions*. If you're using your AdWords campaign to advertise yourself as a face-to-face trainer, then a user in Pakistan that clicks on your ad is a wasted dime for you. Google allows you to specify a country, territory, region, or city for each ad campaign.

- *Choose keywords carefully*. For a supplement that burns fat, the keywords "fat," "weight loss," and "diet" are not specific. The keywords "lipase," "liver fat-burning enzymes," and "Ben Greenfield weight loss" are specific. Google has a free keyword tool that will help you generate keyword lists.

- *Track your ad effectiveness*. The Google system will automatically rotate ads within a certain ad group and display the better performing ads more often. Google also has a website optimizer, which is a tool that allows you to test different versions of text, images, and layout on your landing page, showing which webpage content resulted in the best return on investment. You also have full access to account statistics, which includes information on cost-per-conversion, clicks, and impressions. Google Analytics will help you analyze what people are doing at your site and if they are actually purchasing after clicking on an ad.

- Finally, you can use affiliate-marketing ads as a highly effective way to make money with your website.

Suppose that I know Joe over at NutritionalSupplementsRUs.com. Joe sells an entire line of nutritional supplements that I frequently recommend to my clients and personally endorse and use. In turn, Joe sends clients my way to purchase my services and books. After some time, I realize that many of my clients go to Joe's store and purchase his supplements, but I have no way of knowing how many, I have no way of getting paid for my referrals, and Joe also has no way of tracking our mutually beneficial relationship. So, I send Joe the sample letter outlined in Figure 4-1.

I highly recommend the article at http://www.associateprograms.com/articles/175/1/How-to-start-an-affiliate-program for a comprehensive look at the various software and online affiliate programs that exist to make your job easier. Once again, although it isn't mentioned in that particular article, www.1shoppingcart.com comes to the rescue for me, since I can easily create an ad or banner, generate code using 1shoppingcart's affiliate software and send it to any affiliate, along with a special

Hi Joe,

I'm interested in setting up an affiliate link to NutritionalSupplementsRUs.com from my newsletter and website, which receives 28,000-32,000 hits per month. Basically, we would need a method to track the number of hits from my website that result in sales on your website, then set-up a small three to five percent royalty payback. Depending on who your web service provider is, it would be very easy to create an affiliate link for these purposes. Let me know if you are interested in doing this and I can help you get it set up. It'd be a great way for us to benefit from each other.

The website www.1shoppingcart.com is a great tool to use if you don't have affiliate set-up options through your current web-hosting provider. I plan to add a "supplements" link from http://www.pacificfit.net, featuring supplements more extensively in my newsletter, and also propose to launch several websites over the next year, featuring my books and DVDs, which could potentially provide you with quite a bit of added traffic and exposure.

In exchange for such a royalty setup, I could provide NutritionalSupplementsRUs.com with a very high wholesale discount on my Book/DVD package "100 Ways to Boost Your Metabolism," which features many of the ingredients currently used in your featured products. You can then use this book as a marketing tool to include with your supplements to new customers.

If you'd like, as a certified sports nutritionist, I can also make myself available as a speaker or advisor for NutritionalSupplementsRUs.com special events.

In summary, Let me know if you are interested in setting up an affiliate link from my website, and if you'd like to have inexpensive access to using my book as a way to market your products.

Thanks,
Ben Greenfield

Figure 4-1

script that they copy and paste into their website. The affiliate program at www.1shoppingcart.com will automatically track how many people click on my advertisement on my affiliate's website and end up at my website to make a purchase. I then receive an automatic e-mail at the end of each month that tells me which affiliates I need to pay and how much. Of course, any affiliate whose ads that I run receive the same paycheck notice, that 87 people clicked through from bengreenfieldfitness.com and purchased a total of $1764.54 worth of product. So this month, you write Ben Greenfield a check for $88. You have 10 affiliates, and the money you make while sleeping begins to add up. You have 100 affiliates, and life is good.

This approach is direct marketing that works for targeted advertising, and works in reverse as an alternate income stream. It can generate thousands of dollars of automated monthly revenue from your website. How do you think a website like bengreenfieldfitness.com can afford to function from the free podcasts, videos, and blogs? My affiliate ads, of course—they pay big.

Your List

Every effective marketer understands the importance of a list. Your list is your lifeblood. It contains detailed contact information for every client that has ever visited your website and purchased a product or signed up for a newsletter or any other special program that you've advertised.

You can build your list the wrong way. In the same way that magazines can sell subscriber information, there are websites that sell e-mail contact information. That's right—you can buy your list. However, don't do it, because it is a great way to make a lot of people very upset with you, and a great way to turn yourself into a universally recognized spammer. Instead, you must build your list slowly and surely. When you first begin your website, your list will be small. However…

- If you get written permission from all your face-to-face and online clients to send them occasional e-mails, your list will begin to form.
- If you keep track of the e-mails of users who have purchased your online products, your list will grow a bit quicker.
- If you have a newsletter opt-in feature on your home page that asks a user for their e-mail address and name, in exchange for a free subscription to your helpful e-mail newsletter, your list will grow even faster.
- If you have Web 2.0 and people not only subscribe to your newsletter, but also to your podcast, videos, and blog postings, *your list growth will skyrocket!*

I use a combination of the newsletter and autoresponder feature from www.1shoppingcart.com to generate my list. The following is how I built 4168 subscribers in 11 months at Pacific Elite Fitness, legally and quickly, ensuring that my e-mails were not filtered as spam:

- At my homepage is a centrally placed message that reads:
    "Sign up for the Pacific Elite Fitness newsletter, a weekly publication full of fitness and nutrition tips, training and coaching discounts, and workout challenges. Click here for newsletter archives. The newsletter arrives from newsletter@pacificfit.net, so it is recommended to add this e-mail to your address book so it is not filtered as spam."

- Below this message is a form to type in the name and e-mail and press submit. 1shoppingcart.com provides me with a script that I can just copy and paste to my website to have this form appear. The nice part is that the newsletter section of 1shoppingcart.com is set up to *automatically associate each name with each e-mail address*, so when I send out a mass e-mail newsletter, it contains a personalized greeting at the top of each newsletter that reads "Dear [name]." This is a great way to add a personal touch to your messages.

- Upon subscribing, the user receives a follow-up e-mail that requires him to click on a link to confirm his subscription. This is called an "opt-in feature" and ensures that your e-mails will not be filtered as spam or junk mail. It's technically considered necessary web etiquette, just in case a third party typed in that user's e-mail. This e-mail also reminds the user to add the e-mail address newsletter@pacificfit.net to their address book, further ensuring that my newsletters will actually show up in their legitimate e-mail inbox.

- Anytime, anyone, anywhere has any inquiry about personal training or triathlon coaching, I am sure to tell them to sign-up for the free newsletter at some point in our conversation. Always remember to include the word FREE when you mention your newsletter. It's just like handing out your business card—except every person hands you back a card with their e-mail address and permission to contact them.

I use my list for tons of different marketing techniques, including the following:
- Provide high quality content that differs from a blog, since I can design my newsletter in HTML format and have it download to an e-mail and appear very similar to a webpage, with images, links, banners, tables, etc.
- Advertise monthly specials on my information products, coaching, or training
- Generate ad revenue from affiliates with click-through affiliate ads on the newsletter
- Feature sponsors from my triathlon racing-support team
- Enhance my network-marketing businesses
- Barter with other online marketers for swapping our ads on each other's lists

Always be building your list. Someday, you'll look back, as I did, and be genuinely amazed at how half a dozen personal training clients morphed into thousands and thousands of personal e-mail contacts. And these aren't "junk" contacts. These are people that have signed up and opted in to your newsletter, and are legitimately interested in your product. This gives you a huge advantage.

Domain-Building Technique

If you're Web 2.0-izing your web presence, you're probably going to end up with multiple websites. As I mentioned earlier, you can find a web host for your unique website for as little as five bucks a month. That's 60 dollars a year. Not bad, but if you have five, 10, or 20 unique websites, this expense quickly adds up.

This point is where add-on domains come in. Call or e-mail your web host and explain to them that you have a new website that you want to start, but rather than purchasing a separate domain for that website's domain name, you want to add on the domain to your currently existing website. Any host can do it and they'll know what you're talking about.

Typical add-on domain costs range from $5 to $10 per year! For example, I have a domain name called bengreenfitness.com. I have 12 other websites that I run as add-on domains under this website. Normally, that would cost me $1080 per year without add-on domains. Instead, *using the add-on domain technique, I pay $120 per year.*

One such add-on domain is shape21.com. I can have a separate e-mail, separate web URL and separate pages for shape21.com, but it is actually shadowed behind the domain name bengreenfieldfitness.com. So if you type shape21.com into your browser, it will go to the Shape21 website, but you can also type in bengreenfieldfitness.shape21.com and it will go to the Shape21 website.

When I edit my website, I can log in to the server using the same username, password, and server information that I use to access bengreenfieldfitness.com, but I have a separate folder for shape21.com where I upload all my Shape21 pages. It's seamless, smooth, and an inexpensive way to expand your web empire.

5

Outsourcing

Time is finite. In this chapter, you'll learn how to exponentially increase the effectiveness of your expertise by utilizing other people to inexpensively do much of the busy work for you. Your time is valuable, whether researching exercise topics, creating websites, sending relevant articles to your client base, assisting in exercise photo and video creation, and submitting your fitness articles and press releases to media sources. This chapter teaches you two incredibly effective methods that get this work done for you, inexpensively or free, so that you can spend your valuable time earning your top dollars.

Outsourcing Defined

So far, you've learned quite a bit in this book about various techniques that you can use to enhance your bottom line as a personal trainer. Chapters 3 and 4, particularly, present dozens of different tips and tricks for web utilization of your training expertise.

However, in between training face-to-face clients, teaching boot camps, managing a budding public-speaking career, and designing a corporate-wellness program, do you actually have the personal time to implement Google ad campaigns, YouTube viral video marketing, and hundreds of online article submissions? Furthermore, even if you do have the personal time, wouldn't you rather spend that time actually doing things that you enjoy, like playing in a softball league, learning new riffs on your guitar, studying red wine, or training for triathlons?

People often ask me how I manage to manage with the tiny, but collectively significant, income streams that trickle into the top salary that I command as a personal trainer. This chapter reveals one of my prime secrets and my technique for managing those streams—*outsourcing*.

Technically, outsourcing is subcontracting a process, such as design or manufacturing, to a third-party source. This is typically done to lower your time investment, and allow you to spend your resources elsewhere, thus making more efficient use of a finite number of minutes. But I like to simply think of outsourcing as getting other people to do my grunt work or busy work for me as inexpensively as possible.

With the seamless communication now available in the information age, outsourcing has become simple enough for anyone to do. In this chapter, I share both electronic and non-electronic forms of outsourcing that you can use to decrease the amount of time you spend performing first, work that is long and tedious, but takes no highly specialized skill or expertise, or second, work that takes a high amount of skill and expertise in a field with which you are not familiar and would spend countless hours familiarizing yourself with to become even remotely competent.

It is important to understand one important concept. It's actually going to be quite mentally tough for you to outsource if you are micromanager *and* a learner, which means that you like to have a high amount of control of every aspect of your business or you like to learn how to do things that you could probably hire other people to do for you in the first place. If you possess either of these characteristics, you need to learn how to let go and devote your time and expertise elsewhere.

After all, what would you rather be doing with your workday: one, learning HTML programming, or two, having a rich executive pay you top dollars to shed a few pounds? More importantly, when you get off work at the end of the day, would you rather be designing online ads to run on Google or playing catch with your kids or taking your significant other out to a new downtown club? The key to outsourcing is to let the reins loose, or at least hand a few of them over, then sit back and enjoy the process of having somebody else do some of the driving.

Virtual Assistants

Virtual assistants are online subcontractors who you can hire to do your jobs. The typical jobs for which you would hire a virtual assistant include:
- Website-page design (probably the most popular and the most financially-sensible work for you to outsource)
- E-book cover design (making your e-books or audio products look like real books or DVDs)
- Online-article submitting (see following example)
- Research for specific clients (actually having someone research the latest nutrition or fitness articles relevant to one of your specific client demographics, then e-mailing those articles to each of your specified clients in that demographic, with a pre-written message from you)
- Logo and business card design
- Ghostwriting (you can give someone a basic outline and actually have them research and write your article for you)
- Search-engine optimization and creation of keywords for your website
- Google ad campaign design, management, and statistical analysis

At any one time, I have three to four virtual assistants completing projects for me, while I sleep, for anywhere from $3 to $12 per hour. For example, say I have somewhere around 100 fitness articles that I've written in various newsletters, gym postings, and local newspapers. I want to propagate this entire body of articles across the web in order to enhance my expert status and improve my credibility and popularity. However, I don't have time to visit the hundreds of article submission websites that appear on the Internet and submit these articles one-by-one. Sure, software such as "article submission robots" exists, but they tend to quickly allow websites to label your e-mails as spam, since the robots rely on the highly impersonal, mass-submission shotgun approach. I want to have a real person submit my articles for me, and my little sister just won't cut it. Following is a step-by-step explanation of how I approach this problem:

- I go to a website that features a large number of sub-contractors whose qualifications and ratings I can view. My favorite websites are www.elance.com and www.odesk.com. Both websites allow me to create a "project" proposal that is then posted for bidding by various subcontractors. I can invite specific subcontractors to bid on my project, or simply allow anyone to bid.

- When I create my project description, I am as specific as possible. This is mostly because the majorities of virtual assistants are from outside the country and are not highly proficient in English. I don't want anyone misunderstanding or charging me for a project that is way outside the scope of what I actually need. Figure 5-1 is a sample-project proposal for online-article submission of articles featured at Pacific Elite Fitness:

- I am then given the option, prior to posting my project, to include the amount I am willing to pay, whether I'd like the project bid on a hourly or per-project basis, how I would like to pay, and other important contract terms. Upon posting the bid, I will be inundated over the next 48 hours or so with anywhere from 10 to 30 bids for my project. I will choose the bid that combines the most competent provider and the best price. I will then take money from my credit card and deposit it into an online-escrow account that releases funds when both parties have satisfactorily agreed upon project completion.

- Voila! One week later, I have 117 fitness and nutrition articles floating on the web, and my Google search ranking improves dramatically, as well as my online training inquiries. Both Elance and oDesk include messaging capabilities that allow me to seamlessly interact with my virtual assistants throughout the entire process, although I often use the free Skype service to talk live with my virtual assistants in India and Pakistan.

I'll spend the 117 hours I would have personally spent on that project learning some new guitar tricks. The virtual assistant will complete the project in a total of 13 hours, for $6 per hour. Was that worth $78? Absolutely. As a matter of fact, I am willing to pay a virtual assistant up to $50 per hour, as I value my time at approximately $100 per hour. What value do you place on your time?

Hi,

I run an online-triathlon coaching and personal-training website that has a free database of articles that I've written, which are archived on my website at www.pacificfit.net. The articles range from writings that I've included as part of my newsletters to some that I've simply published to my website. The articles can be found on the left side of the page at both: www.pacificfit.net/fitness.html and www.pacificfit.net/triathletes.html.

The website has about 100-120 articles. I need you to take every individual article on my website and submit it to as many online-article websites as possible, in order to increase traffic to my website and establish myself as an online expert in fitness and nutrition. Examples of websites that I'd like my articles published to would include:

www.addme.com	www.articlesumbissions.com	www.family-content.com
www.allthewebsites.org	www.articlewarehouse.com	www.findbusinessarticles.com
www.amazines.com	www.articleworld.net	www.freezinesite.com
www.articlealley.com	www.authorconnection.com	www.fresh-articles.com
www.articlebin.com	www.awebhostingprovider.com	www.goarticles.com
www.articlecentral.com	www.businesstoolchest.com	www.ideamarketers.com
www.articlecity.com	www.buzzle.com	www.isnare.com
www.article-directory.net	www.commonconnections.com	www.marketingpitbull.com
www.article-emporium.com	www.connectionteam.com	www.searchwarp.com
www.articlefinders.com	www.constant-content.com	www.tritopics.com
www.articlesfactory.com	www.easyarticles.com	www.uniterra.com
www.articlessource.com	www.ezinearticles.com	www.womens-netnews.com

Obviously, this list is not a comprehensive list, but a good starting point. Most importantly, I want my articles to appear on as many websites as possible.

You'll have to make sure the articles are formatted correctly, and you'll probably have to include my bio with many of the articles. Upon receiving your bid, I can send you my bio via e-mail. The other thing that you'll have to ensure is that my website URL (www.pacificfit.net) appears in every article, if possible. If you only have the opportunity to use one URL, then use www.pacificfit.net, but if you have the opportunity to include multiple URLs, then please also include www.champsportsmed.com.

I need all articles submitted within seven days, with a full Excel®-spreadsheet report that shows which websites received which articles.

Thank you,
Ben Greenfield

Figure 5-1

Interns

When I completed my undergraduate coursework, I was required to satisfy a certain number of internship and practicum hours. The way that the education process works, I was not actually compensated for these hours. Instead, I received something that a student can find even more valuable than money, and that is "credits."

Students will go to quite a degree of trouble to receive credits. Credits are like career currency. You can use them as points towards different majors, and when you graduate with that major, you are worth a higher salary. So credits have a good deal of inherent value.

One summer, I spent nearly 40 hours per week digitizing biomechanical high-speed video on an outdated computer system. Sure, a slick software program could have done this all for me, but I didn't care, because every hour I spent in that chair would award me more credits. The next summer, I did the very same thing, but this time in front of a liquid-chromatography machine collecting bacterial samples.

It wasn't until after graduating with my bachelor's degree that I realized this very same uncontrollable hunger for credits that I displayed as a young college intern and that I somehow used to justify enormous number of hours spent performing boring busywork could actually be used as a type of karma. That's right, I could get interns to do busywork for me, in the same way that I eagerly did it for my professors and internship coordinators. What goes around comes around. Also, ever since beginning my master's degree study as manager of a wellness program at a popular university, I have used interns to complete countless examples of busywork that are highly educational and very effective, but that I'd rather not spend the time doing myself.

Whereas virtual assistants typically ask for money up front, college interns are oh-so-happy to *complete your jobs for free*. The following is how to find your personal-training interns for fitness and nutrition credits:

- Contact the sport science or nutrition departments for each of your local universities. Ask for the e-mail address of the internship coordinator. If more than one exists (often various professors oversee specific internship programs), then simply ask for the individual who manages interns in your specific niche market. For example, you can ask, "I have an internship opportunity for a student who is pursuing coursework that may cover the topic of periodization for endurance athletes. Do you know who would coordinate this type of internship?"

- Once you have the contact information, present the sample e-mail or personal letter shown in Figure 5-2 to the internship coordinator.

- When you receive the sudden influx of students who are eager to complete your tasks, you'll need to fill out a minimal amount of paperwork, recording their hours and rating their people skills, knowledge, performance, etc. This task will take you about five minutes.

Dear Professor X,

As a certified-exercise professional operating out of the local Spokane community, I specialize in providing periodized-resistance training and swim, bike, run programs to the local endurance athlete population. My facility operates as a limited-liability corporation, and we are fully insured and licensed to provide high quality coaching and training to our clientele.

As part of an ongoing relationship-building effort in our community, I would like to offer an opportunity for your students who may be interested in pursing careers as endurance coaches, physiologists, biomechanists, or personal trainers. An internship or practicum hours with our facility would provide a student with a wealth of practical information to use in their future career studies, and I have several positions available.

Please contact me with the details of how we can set up an internship and practicum program in the field of endurance-exercise science with your department. I am looking forward to a mutually beneficial relationship between our business and your university. Please contact me with any questions.

Sincerely,
Ben Greenfield
MS, CSCS

Figure 5-2

Utilizing this method, I've used interns for the following:

- Writing basic personal-training programs for non-complicated clients, or adding colorful pictures and descriptions to each basic exercise for the client handout

- Designing standardized health-history questionnaires and exercise-evaluation procedures to be used during consultations or initial client meetings

- Word processing client workout notes that I've scribbled on a notepad during a workout session

- Creating simple ads and posts for special programs or personal-training deals, then copying them and plastering them wherever I instruct

- Overseeing my personal-training sessions while I work on my computer in the background. This is especially useful for students who need personal training hours to complete a certification.

- Researching exercise methods and techniques that I've heard of and need to know more about. I've received entire folders with printed articles on the details, pros and cons of vibration training, aquatic plyometrics, $\dot{V}O_{2max}$ field testing, and compound sets.

- Submitting my exercise videos to the blogs, MySpace and Facebook pages of all their exercise-science schoolmates, who then ensure my videos become virally distributed across the Internet with their valuable social networking skills

- Cleaning my gym equipment (much more thoroughly than I'd do it when rushed between clients)

- Calling my clients to remind them of their appointments, thus giving my business an even more personal touch

- Warming-up, cooling-down, and stretching my clients. This often doesn't take expertise, just a helping hand. If an intern is learning something such as a proprioceptive neuromuscular facilitation, I'll have them practice when stretching a client under my supervision.

- Writing press releases and submitting to newspaper editors. Press releases are standardized and easy to write. Interns can easily learn this skill, and enhance your marketing and visibility.

- Creating my booths for health expos, including copying handouts, setting up tables, decorating the booth, working the actual booth, and cleaning up afterward

- Properly formatting my exercise photos and videos and uploading them via FTP to my web server

- Getting me lunch when I'm busy. It is truly wonderful to finish a personal training session or public-speaking appointment and have a tasty sandwich magically appear on my desk.

As you can see, the number of hours that I've saved are countless—*and 100% free of charge.*

If you have one university in your town, that is enough to establish your internship program. The beauty of the university-relationship program is that once it is up and running, word spreads, and at the beginning of each quarter, semester, and any other important milestone in the academic calendar year, you'll receive flurries of e-mail and phone calls from eager students wanting to satisfy their internship and practicum hours—so, put them to work!

6

Supplements

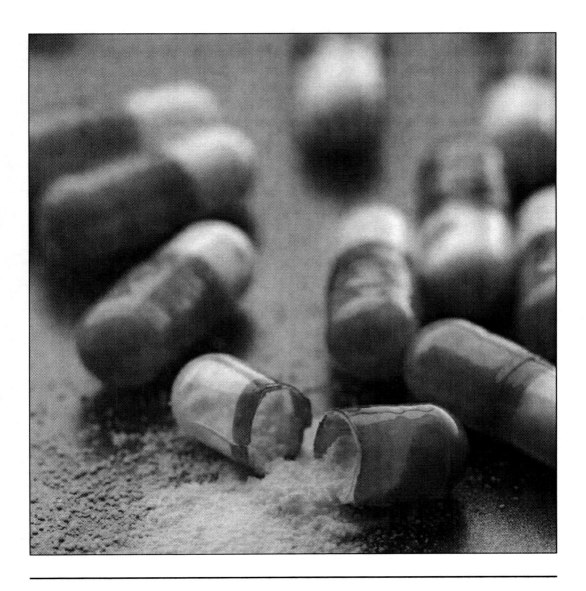

The dietary supplement industry is huge, and personal trainers are in a perfect position to receive a very large slice of the pie. You can command an enormous salary through direct sales, supplement network marketing, affiliate sales, and online distribution. As an educated health professional, you'll learn how to get started in the supplement-representation industry—one unique method for using your expertise to receive a lifetime of free supplements for your own consumption and for selling to your clients, and another unique product-representation technique that sets you up for a high percentage royalty kickback.

The Case for Supplements

Imagine automatically giving yourself a 40 dollar per session raise for all of your weekly clients, simply by handing them a bottle of pills as they walk out the door and adding the charge to their automatically debited account for that month. Furthermore, imagine that, during this same week, 20 of your clients and customers log in to your website and purchase over 30 additional 40 dollar pill bottles direct from you, using a free shipping code you advertised in your e-mail newsletter. While at your website, a handful of these same customers click one of your supplement-affiliate logos and purchase 200 dollars worth of products from your affiliate's website, which pays you a 10 percent kickback.

During the same week, three of the clients to whom you directly sold a specific multi-vitamin capsule decide that they actually want to share this supplement with their friends. Rather than selling the multi-vitamins directly to their friends, you set these people up with the ability to do it themselves through a multi-vitamin network-marketing company. You receive 12 percent of the profit generated when these people order their multi-vitamins to distribute to their friends, and another six percent of the profit from any of these friends who decide to begin purchasing these vitamins themselves. This week, that process nets you $82.

Finally, an information e-book that you created in the prior month, in which you featured one of your favorite weight-loss supplements, is actually being sold by that same weight-loss supplement company, and they're paying you a royalty kickback of six percent for the 13 $29.99 e-books that sold that week.

Do the math. Your dietary supplement "side" business is generating $1,725.39 per week for you, for about one hour worth of extra order and sales work on your part and another 30 minutes spent at Fed-Ex, shipping supplements with your discount-business account (unless you outsource this job to an intern).

Most people simply love dietary supplements. There is something addicting about popping a pill and imagining it causing unique biochemical reactions within your body that suddenly boosts performance, weight loss, mental clarity, energy, or any other desired objective. And once people start popping, they don't stop—neither does the cash flow.

Don't get me wrong. I do not endorse the use of any supplements that have not been adequately researched. I do not endorse the use of any supplements that have not been produced by a certified manufacturing process facility and are not World Anti-Doping Association approved. I do not endorse the use of any supplements for which my clients do not understand the basic purpose or mechanism of action. *You must know what you endorse*, and you do not want to blindly push every pill on the planet.

Over the course of the past decade, I've gradually built up a library of the supplements that I have personally found to be most safe and effective for my clients, and I've developed an affiliate relationship with every company that represents those supplements, thus ensuring that anytime I recommend that supplement to a client, I am making money. This is not bad ethics. This is good sense. If you were going to recommend the supplement anyway, you might as well profit from it.

You'll find that most of your clients are very receptive to taking dietary supplements to help achieve their goals, but some are not. Following is an overview of how I make a case to those supplement-resistant clients:

- I'll first direct them to a previous article that I've written on the topic, available on my website (refer to Figure 6-1).

- After getting this information into my client's hands, I will then use the "puppy sale." The puppy sale derives its title from the way that a pet shop would sell you a new pet. You go to the pet shop, see the cutest little puppy in its cage, staring up at you with big pleading eyes. You "ooh" and "aah," but then realize that you probably can't afford to add a puppy into your lifestyle. This is when the pet shop salesman steps in with the puppy-sale technique, placing the puppy into your arms and exclaiming, "Just take him home and play with him for a few days. If you don't like him, bring him on back, and we'll find him a new home." Once you've brought that puppy home, how likely is it that you'll return him to the pet shop after a few days of cuddling and playing? The chances are slim to none. The same goes for supplements. I simply hand the bottle to a client, tell them to try it for a week or a month, and to bring the bottle back if they don't see results. Since I only endorse products that actually work, I have a return rate of under one percent—that's the puppy sale.

- In addition, for my online-personal training or triathlon-coaching clients, I have an e-mail that I send out that is similar to that in Figure 6-2.

If you eat your fruits and vegetables, expose yourself to adequate sunlight, get plenty of sleep, and stay well hydrated, your body shouldn't really need a supplemental source of vitamins and minerals, right? Wrong. Following are five powerful reasons that you need to take supplements, no matter how healthy your lifestyle may be:

- Nutrient depletion in the soil. Modern farming techniques utilize fertilizers that actually deplete the soil of essential nutrients. Agriculture relies on the elements in the soil for absorption of proper amounts of minerals, and when this process is interrupted, the plant does not contain essential minerals and cannot form essential vitamins. And if the plant doesn't have it then you're not going to get it from eating the plant.

- Your ability to absorb nutrients from food actually decreases as you age. So, while growing children should absolutely be taking a multivitamin to support healthy tissue and bone formation, supplementation becomes equally important for the older population. Sure, you could just eat more food, but this factor introduces a problem with caloric balance. Beware that many medications also interfere with proper nutrient absorption.

- Commercial harvesting, shipping processes, long-term food storage, processing, and addition of preservatives degrades the nutrient content of food. Therefore, unless you're eating a very fresh plant, it is a far different species at consumption than it was when initially harvested. In addition, compounds added to the food during many of these processes, such as MSG, saccharine, nutrasweet, splenda, colorings, and flavors will increase your body's need for nutrients to deal with these damaging synthetic derivatives.

- Pesticides, herbicides, and chemicals found in the modern food supply are combined with chemicals in water, and environmental contamination from elements, such as degraded plastic, air pollution from carbon monoxide, lead, and mercury. These synergistic elements vastly increase our need for extra vitamins, minerals, and nutrients to combat formation of free radicals and the attack upon our metabolism and immune system.

- Exercise increases nutrient needs. Are you an athlete or frequent exerciser? The vast amount of extra oxygen and energy used by active individuals will necessitate nutrient consumption that far exceeds the typical RDA of the average population. Consuming just the stated RDA can actually limit your athletic performance.

So what are you waiting for? Get your hands on a highly effective dietary-supplement protocol today. Speaking with your personal trainer is a great place to start. Your trainer can help you choose the supplements that are most safe and effective for your specific body, goals, and needs.

Figure 6-1

Dear client,

Following is a list of supplements that I currently take. Some of these supplements would be necessary only for an individual who is breaking their body down with high amounts of marathon-like training, Ironman, or heavy bodybuilding. I put an asterisk next to these particular items. The asterisk indicates that the supplement is for endurance athletes or heavy exercisers. The rest of the supplements are fantastic daily additions to a healthy diet.

I've also included special discount codes that can get you deals on some of the supplements. I encourage you to speak with your physician about how these supplements will interact with any pharmaceutical medications you may currently be taking.

- Hammer Gel® Race Caps—improves mitochondrial activity (slow twitch muscle oxidation capacity); also great for controlling effects of aging. Order from www.hammernutrition.com, discount code 80244.
- Hammer Gel Recoverite®—protein/carb. Take after training sessions when whole food protein/carbohydrate source is not logistically convenient. Order from www.hammernutrition.com, discount code 80244.
- Hammer Gel Perpeetuum—three+ hour training sessions. Order from www.hammernutrition.com, discount code 80244.
- Hammer Gel Heed®—sub three-hour training sessions. Order from www.hammernutrition.com, discount code 80244.
- *Hammer Gel E-caps—electrolytes during race/longer training sessions. Order from www.hammernutrition.com, discount code 80244.
- Carlson's Norwegian Salmon Oil—omega-3 fatty acids for antioxidant and joint health. Order from www.hammernutrition.com, discount code 80244
- Nuun—electrolytes, load for three days prior to race to improve intramuscular sodium content. Order from www.nuun.com, discount code XXXXX.
- *Millennium Sports Kreaceps—creatine. Load for seven days prior to race to improve muscular force contraction; primarily for wattage on bike. Order from www.millenniumsports.net or by calling 1-800-249-7918, discount code XXXXX.
- *Millennium Sports Citruvol—citrulline. Load for seven days prior to race to improve lactic acid clearance; speeds up ammonia reduction, decreases burn in legs. Order from www.millenniumsports.net or by calling 1-800-249-7918, discount code XXXXX.
- *Millennium Sports Carnage—alanine. Load for seven days prior to race to increase intramuscular nitric oxide levels; enhances glucose and muscular oxygen uptake. Order from www.millenniumsports.net or by calling 1-800-249-7918, discount code XXXXX.
- Millennium Sports Cordgyen 5 or the new Cordgyen VO_2—cordyceps. Load for 30 days prior to race to improve adrenal activation of lung tissue; improves overall VO_{2max}. Order from www.millenniumsports.net or by calling 1-800-249-7918, discount code XXXXX.
- Wicked Fast® RecoverEase—branched-chain amino acids. Take four on training days to enhance recovery; take eight after a race. Order from www.recover-ease.com.
- Impax® ProstElan—prostate anti-inflammatory for the long time spent in the saddle. Order as "autoship" from 1-800-78-IMPAX. Tell them your enroller number is 13372 and your sponsor number is 12228.
- Impax EnerPrime—superfood multi-vitamin. Too many benefits to list, but primarily for immune-system integrity (I rarely get sick since taking it). Order as "autoship" from 1-800-78-IMPAX. Tell them your enroller number is 13372 and your sponsor number is 12228.
- Impax DeltaE—only take as an ergogenic aid for caffeine and vitamin B12 megadose content 30 to 45 minutes prior to a race. Order as "autoship" from 1-800-78-IMPAX. Tell them your enroller number is 13372 and your sponsor number is 12228.

Yours in health,
Ben Greenfield

Figure 6-2

In the example, I've "X'ed" out special codes which that company may not want me to share in this book. However, the important part is that I receive a kickback or free product anytime some orders are placed using those codes. There is an even more effective and automated way to accomplish this objective, called affiliate tracking, which I'll teach later in this chapter. Furthermore, in this chapter, we'll examine a number of different methods you can use to dramatically improve your income with dietary supplement representation. It takes more than just a direct-sales approach (ordering random pill bottles from wholesale distributors, then selling them yourself), and I'll teach you many more tricks than that.

Direct Sales

Direct sales of a nutritional supplement are perhaps the easiest to understand and the most logistically-feasible place to start. In this scenario, you simply re-sell nutritional supplements for a higher price than you acquired them. It's an easy way to make a few bucks here and there, but a bit labor intensive in relation to your actual profit. There's also often an ethical dilemma of you being forced to order fat-burning product X because it is on wholesale, when you've actually only studied or had experience with fat-burning product Y, which is not on wholesale. The wholesale-supplement distributors will often try to sell you on a product for which you have very little experience, so it can be dangerous for both you and your clients. Should you find a supplement distributor that carries a large line of products that you actually trust, then this approach is a good way to go. I prefer the following sources for ordering a product:

- www.bodybuilding.com
- www.a1nutrition.com
- My local super supplements outlet
- www.gnc.com and my local GNC outlet

It is very important that you don't just talk to any random person on the phone or via e-mail when you order your supplements from a company. You must establish a relationship with a sales rep if possible. This way, you can be notified when there are special discounts on products that you have ordered or for which you have shown interest in the past. You can also arrange special deals like free shipping.

The best way to make sure you connect with a live person who can handle your account (since you plan on making this a big part of your training business) is to actually call the company and specifically say something like, "Hi, this is Ben Greenfield and I run a highly successful nutritional supplement sales business based out of Spokane, WA. We are a mid-to-large volume distributor of nutritional supplements as part of our personal training business, and I'd like to establish a relationship with a representative from your company for all future orders that we plan on making from your company. Can you connect me with the right person?"

It doesn't matter whether you're really a "mid-to-large volume distributor." This comment will just make sure that they see dollar signs and get you to the right person. Besides, volume is all relative, right?

Following are the steps for direct sales to your face-to-face clients:

- *Stock and display your product*. When it arrives to your gym, studio, home, or wherever else you train your clients, don't just put it away in a cupboard or refrigerator and pull it out when you want to sell it. Out of sight is out of mind. Keep it in a location where your clients will see it and ask questions about it. Go to a website like http://www.business.com and search for "display cases and racks" to view a host of different businesses that sell affordable display cases for your supplements. For $50 to $150 you can have a nice little countertop acrylic-display case that showcases your supplements and makes them look much better than they would compared to rolling around in the vegetable crisper of your gym refrigerator.

- *Work the product into your client's programs as a necessity*. In the same way that exercise, proper nutrition, and lifestyle management are not options, supplements should also be a required component of a client's membership in your personal-training program. I personally have three different supplements that all my weight-loss clients are required to take, period. I simply tell them that the program will not work at maximum effectiveness unless they take a specific multi-vitamin, fat burner, and carb-resistance blend. This is a true statement. And I sell them that blend. It costs each of those clients about $100 a month, and I am 100 percent certain they can afford that amount if they are paying the amount I charge for personal training.

- *Enhance your consults and single sessions with supplements*. Just because you're meeting with an individual just one time to talk about nutrition or exercise doesn't mean that they can't walk out the door without supplements. Why not turn that $100 per hr consult into $149.99 by giving a five-minute tour of your supplement-display case before or after the session? As you meet and greet and meander toward your office, simply say, "Oh yes, we also feature a full line of supplements..." Then continue by giving a brief explanation of each. It's a great way to showcase your knowledge and make a potential sale, or to generate conversation during your ensuing consultation.

The alternative method to face-to-face direct sales is by featuring products on your website. At my website www.pacificfit.net, I rely primarily on direct sales of supplements, with a small network marketing and affiliate component, whereas at www.bengreenfieldfitness.com, I heavily rely on affiliate marketing click-throughs. The tricky part about direct online sales is that you are personally responsible for shipping all orders (whereas with your face-to-face clients, you simply hand them the supplement).

Following are some tips for direct-online sales through your website:

- *Include discount codes.* In your online newsletter or blog, include discount codes that allow sales of specific supplements, or free-shipping codes. Often, I will just jack up the price of a supplement, include a free-shipping code, and enhance my sales two to three times versus the lower priced, non-free shipping supplement. Both discount codes and free-shipping codes can easily be applied to any individual product using www.1shoppingcart.com. This technique will not only enhance your supplement sales, but also ensure that your newsletters are actually read on a regular basis, as people try to find out what's "on-sale" for that month. On the flipside, don't offer big sales on your personal training. Would your physician offer discounts on office visits? Rarely, because it cheapens the experience.

- *Batch your shipped products.* There's no rule that you have to ship in 24 or 48 hours, especially if you're only selling two to three bottles per day. Wait until the end of the week to make that special trip to Fed-Ex for shipping. You can also outsource your shipping to an intern or third party, simply setting up orders to automatically forward to the third party's e-mail folder.

- *Include pictures of your supplement on the order page.* Remember, an image can be worth a thousand words. For the same reason that you need to design your e-books to look like real books, you need to include actual photographs of the bottles, because people want to see a "real" product. Take the photos yourself against a solid, neutral background or, better yet, just use the manufacturer's photos.

- *Don't include links that are not set up as affiliates.* If the links are not set up as affiliates for you to get paid on click-throughs, then don't include them with the actual supplement manufacturer's website. Instead, cut and paste any necessary product information onto your own website. If someone "leaves" your website and finds a better price as they're surfing around the manufacturer's website, you've lost the sale. Often, people will buy from you because of your expert status or because of their relationship with you as a client, not because you offer the best price. So, keep them on your site and charge whatever price you desire.

- *Sell products you don't even own.* With your face-to-face direct sales, it can be very difficult to up-sell a supplement to a client, then say, "Just wait a week and I can have it here!" Your client wants to leave with the product in hand, and they're typically not going to want to pre-pay and wait for it to arrive. Your online sales customers, however, have already paid and anticipate having to wait a few days for the product to arrive. If cash flow is an issue and you don't want to be stocking unsold products, then wait for your Internet orders to arrive, then turn around and order from the manufacturer. This method is especially useful if you've arranged a free shipping deal with the personal sales rep from the manufacturer. You do have a personal sales rep, right?

Direct sales are the traditional method for supplement sales, and they work just fine. But there are some other interesting ways to improve your bottom line in the supplement industry, which I'll teach you about in the rest of this chapter.

Network Marketing

Imagine that every month you could receive a series of checks that exceed a thousand dollars. You do nothing for this money. And although network or multi-level marketing has a bad rap among many people who considerate it illegitimate business, you'll find it to be just another effective way to enhance your income stream. If done properly, it is not "pressure sales," but simply good business.

Robert Kiyosaki, a highly successful author and creator of the Rich Dad™ company, has an interesting insight on network marketing. He says that there are two reasons to go into network marketing: one, to help yourself, and two, to help others. More specifically, you need to have the viewpoint that you are helping yourself add additional businesses to your portfolio, and helping others launch their own businesses. You are simply creating additional assets for yourself by feeding on the income stream from other businesses on your "downline," which is represented by individuals who you have helped launch their business.

Suppose you decide that you want to add to your nutritional supplement-income stream via a network-marketing component. You must first find a product. My highest yielding network-marketing supplement is one that I discovered while racing triathlon. It literally took my racing to the next level by reducing my number of sick days during an average year from 14 to 21 days to zero. That's right—I didn't get sick at all, ever, after beginning to take this specific company's superfood multi-vitamin product. In addition, my energy levels were boosted through the roof. I was lucky enough to pick up a sponsorship from the company and receive a large amount of free product (getting "sponsored" is discussed later in this chapter), but upon signing up to be a rep, I had a groundbreaking revelation: *The expert status of a personal trainer places him or her in the unique position to be able to enroll an enormous number of network marketing auto-ship customers.*

What does the "auto-ship" term in this statement mean? Basically, the way that most network marketing companies work is that if you share the product with Jim and he decides to order the product one time via the company's website, you might get a small royalty, say three percent, on Jim's one-time purchase. But if Jim signs up to automatically receive a certain number of products each month via a direct withdrawal from his bank account or credit card, then Jim is now an auto-ship customer, and you receive a larger royalty, say eight percent, of each of Jim's purchases. By signing up for auto-ship, Jim also receives a 20 percent discount on his purchase. Finally, if Jim decides to actually represent the product himself (AKA "distributor" or "rep") and enrolls his friend Jane in an auto-ship program, Jim is now a rep, and you receive 10 percent of each of Jim's purchases and three percent of each of Jane's purchases. Now Jim gets a 25 percent discount on all his purchases. And this type of network marketing can add up to big bucks pretty quickly.

It might take a great deal of pressure from you to convince Jim to become a rep. This is where most people run into trouble with network marketing—they lose friends and customers by pressuring others (i.e., inviting people to their house for dinner then trying to enroll them). But it takes much less convincing for Jim to simply and conveniently auto-ship his orders without actually becoming a rep. This is where a personal trainer has a huge advantage in network marketing: *you don't ever have to worry about pressuring people to become reps* if 300 individuals who receive your wellness newsletter decide to auto-ship themselves your particular network-marketed nutritional supplement. Sure, you never get up to that higher commission level, but it's a great start to begin receiving eight percent commission on a massive number of purchases. Worry about becoming a rep later, if that's something you want to do (which I highly suggest, if you really want to become financially independent in such an enterprise).

This is exactly what happened to me when I began featuring the superfood multi-vitamin in my newsletter. The checks just kept getting bigger and bigger as word spread, and although I eventually started signing up reps (instead of just customers), I started by generating a strong customer base and learning how to gradually build the businesses.

Therefore, you as a personal trainer can engage in this type of network marketing quite successfully—simply sign up as a rep for the company, and go about your networking by using your expert status to sign a high number of auto-ship customers. You'll learn about your products, become a great spokesperson for the supplements, then eventually step it up a notch and begin signing up other reps, if that's something you want to do. By the way, your expert status will only be fully realized if you follow the advice in Chapter 8 on attaining expert status for *both* fitness and nutrition.

Leveraging Your Information Product

In Chapter 8, I introduce a comprehensive overview of how to create and sell information products for big bucks. I also have a unique method of leveraging these information products to actually receive free nutritional supplements or heavy wholesale discounts on nutritional supplements that I can then directly sell to my face-to-face and online customers.

If you currently have an information product, a book on eight highly effective fat burning herbs for instance, you can actually find a nutritional-supplement company that sells products that contain the ingredients that you condone in the book. Make sure it is a company whose products you have tried and trust for your clients and customers. Then make an offer to the company to redesign your book to specifically feature that company's supplements in the introduction and on the topic or chapter pages in your book.

I have successfully used this strategy. One of my books was completely redesigned to feature a specific company's nutritional supplements. After completing the book, I sent it in electronic format to the company, who used one of their large-scale publishing affiliates to reproduce hundreds of copies of my book to feature in their catalog and sell to their customers. I supplied the book to them for free, and now make a royalty on all book sales to their customers. I also receive a limited amount of free products each month, as well as a significant discount on any additional products. I introduce both the free and discounted products to my clients, and also use the product myself. This strategy is very easy to implement and offers you a convenient way to enhance your bottom line in the nutritional supplement industry.

Representing a Product

As a fitness expert, you are in the unique situation of having the opportunity to receive generous sponsorships from fitness and nutrition companies *without* actually having the athletic-prowess or competition resume of the type of athletes or individuals typically sponsored by such a company. All it takes is a good sponsorship letter. Along with full pictures of me racing, a picture of me giving a lecture to a large crowd, and a well-designed color layout, I send something similar to the letter in Figure 6-3 to 10 to 12 potential sponsors every year.

It is important to remember that you don't have to be fast or superior at your sport, or anywhere near the top of your game to succeed in attaining fantastic sponsorships. If you are faster, better, and stronger, then that's wonderful, because you can include your accomplishments as more leverage. But what you really need to emphasize is that you directly influence the purchasing choices of a huge array of individuals through

To whom it may concern,

I am director of sports performance for Champions Sports Medicine, a training facility that provides medical, therapeutic, nutritional, physiologic, and biomechanic services to endurance athletes. In addition, I am president of Pacific Elite Fitness, an endurance sports-coaching service that represents over 75 athletes, with approximately 35,000 website hits per month and a rapidly expanding newsletter and athlete base. I also serve on the board of directors for the Tri-Fusion Triathlon Club, a highly visible club that is literally exploding with growth, and after only one year of existence is the 2007 Triathlon Northwest Club Champion.

In each of these duties, I directly coach, advise, and train hundreds of athletes, and every single one of these individuals relies on me for gear, nutrition, and training recommendations, including specific product brand and store advice. Each year, I teach triathlon-training classes at venues like REI®, local health clubs, private athlete groups, and medical centers, where I also provide product recommendations and reviews based on personal experience.

I received bachelor's and master's degrees in sports science and exercise physiology at University of Idaho, where I was president of the triathlon club and manager of the wellness program. In addition, I hold nationally recognized certifications in strength, conditioning, coaching (NSCA, CSCS, and CPT), Serotta bike fit, International Society of Sports Nutrition, and have over eight years of coaching and training experience. I have been a featured speaker at the IM Coeur D' Alene and IM Hawaii medical conferences. Finally, this year I was voted as the number one personal trainer in the nation by the NSCA.

In 2006, at age 23, I decided to devote more time to triathlon, in order to compete at a higher level and pursue a ranking. On the back side of this letter, I've outlined my 06/07 race season and results. At the end of the '06 season, I was ranked as the number three overall triathlete in the northwest and nominated by the USAT as an All American. In 2007, I have qualified for world championships in Half-IM, IM, and ITU short course, and I am currently ranked number one in Triathlon Northwest—shattering all last year's PRs in every distance. Based on these successes, combined with the number of athletes that I directly influence through coaching, I believe that your company could highly benefit from sponsoring me for the upcoming race season. I am a very vocal and forward person who will vigorously endorse and proudly display your logo on my racing gear, and also utilize and refer to your products in all my lectures and coaching.

I've been impressed with your representation at venues where I compete and I look forward to a continued mutually-beneficial relationship with your company. Thank you for your consideration.

Ben Greenfield

Figure 6-3

your coaching or training, and each of those individuals fits into your potential sponsor's client and customer demographic. With variations of this letter, I now receive free shoes, clothing, nutritional supplements, bicycles, wetsuits, all necessary racing gear, and cash. I race in a very expensive sport for free, and have bigger and better sponsorships than the pros. Never underestimate your power as a niche expert.

Affiliate Sales

Remember that you can use affiliate marketing as a highly-effective way to make money with your nutritional-supplement connections. This marketing is much different than direct sales, since someone else is doing the selling, and you're just receiving a commission when people buy, based on your recommendation.

Refer to the scenario from Chapter 4, with Joe, my friend at NutritionalSupplementsRUs.com. Joe sells an entire line of nutritional supplements that I frequently recommend to my clients and personally endorse and use. In turn, Joe sends clients my way to purchase my services and books. After some time, I realize that many of my clients go to Joe's store and purchase his supplements, but I have no way of knowing how many, I have no way of getting paid for my referrals, and Joe also has no way of tracking our mutually-beneficial relationship, so I send Joe the e-mail outlined in Figure 4-1.

Notice that in this letter, in addition to affiliate set-up, I also use my information product as leverage. For a comprehensive look at the various software and online-affiliate programs that exist to make your job easier I highly recommend the article at http://www.associateprograms.com/articles/175/1/How-to-start-an-affiliate-program. Although it isn't mentioned in that particular article, www.1shoppingcart.com comes to the rescue for me, once again, since I can easily create an ad or banner, generate code using 1shoppingcart's affiliate software, send it to any affiliate along with a special script that they copy and paste into their website, and it will automatically track how many people click on my advertisement on their website and end up at my website to make a purchase. I then receive an automatic e-mail at the end of each month that tells me which affiliates I need to pay and how much. Of course, any affiliate whose ads that I run receive the same paycheck notice that 87 people clicked through from bengreenfieldfitness.com and purchased a total of $1764.54 worth of products, so this month, you write Ben Greenfield a check for $88. You have 10 affiliates, and the money you make while sleeping begins to add up. You have 100 affiliates, and life is good.

Figure 6-4 is another letter that I sent to a list of sponsors and acquaintances in the fitness- and nutrition-product industry, prior to launching a Web 2.0 driven site.

Dear _____,

I have a very exciting announcement and opportunity for your business. In six days, in my most groundbreaking business venture yet, my new fitness and nutrition website will officially launch.

This website is being released in preparation for a nationwide marketing campaign for my personal-training and nutrition services. Building on the anticipated nationwide demand for fitness, nutritional, and wellness advice from me, I am launching a new website as a powerful Web 2.0 technology driven platform, designed to do the following:

- Deliver automatic audio podcasts on diet, fitness, and wellness
- Release weekly syndicated exercise videos and interviews
- Feature a daily blog posting on nutrition and exercise
- Devote a large amount of prime online real estate space to nutrition- and fitness-commercial advertisements, as well as nutrition and fitness affiliates and sponsors

So where do you come in? I want you to be an affiliate of my new website, which means that I want to feature your product in my blogs, podcasts, and videos, and I want you to be able to track the people that discover you on my website and come to your website to purchase your product from you.

To initiate an affiliate program, I simply need you to do me a favor: Please put me in contact with the individual who runs your website, online shopping cart, or e-commerce system so that I can arrange setting your company up as a featured affiliate of my website. It doesn't matter if you currently have an online affiliate program set-up or not, as I will work with your webmaster to make it happen.

That's it! Please contact me with any questions. I'd like to get your affiliate program up and running as soon as possible. As a bonus, once your affiliate program is established, you can use it to advertise on a large number of other websites. Here's to the future!

Ben Greenfield

Figure 6-4

From this letter alone, I secured 12 affiliates. I worked closely with their webmaster to find an affiliate program that worked with the company's current third party shopping-cart system. Once the code was in place, an ad for that company appeared on my website and I now make money every time someone clicks on those ads.

It takes time in the health and fitness industry to discover and build a relationship with potential affiliates. Otherwise, you're just representing a product you know nothing about, and you are potentially selling junk. This method is a great way to get a black hat in an industry where having a white hat is very important. Furthermore, if you have expert status and have a very solid relationship with a particular supplement manufacturer, you can utilize the money-making technique I'll introduce next.

Book/Supplement Tie-In

So, you're an expert, right? In Chapter 8, I'll tell you how to create information products, like books and DVDs, which can help you spread your expertise around the world. But in the specific industry of nutritional supplements, you can use your expertise to land a high-paying book-royalty contract with any supplement manufacturer with which you have a relationship.

Do you remember NO2®? This highly popular nitric-oxide supplement was preceded by an advertising campaign based upon a book that featured NO2-related case studies and testimonials. Popular health and fitness magazines from around the country simply featured the book, not the supplement itself.

This technique created a huge amount of interest for the supplement from the large number of people who noticed and purchased the very affordable book. As a result, when NO2 was finally released, the bottles sold like hotcakes! And they sold at a ridiculous $79.95 per bottle, a very expensive price compared to other similar supplements (like creatine). The guy who invented NO2 is filthy rich. The following process illustrates the three steps that will secure you a big piece of the pie:

- Talk to a nutritional-supplement company with which you have a relationship. It doesn't matter if they are small or large. The important fact is that they must have a forthcoming product that is unique in the nutrition-supplement industry.

- Tell your contact correlation inside the company the very same aforementioned NO2 story. Remember, you must communicate the fact that the book was inexpensive but the supplements are liquid gold.

- Make the following offer: In exchange for a high-royalty percentage on book sales (15 to 20 percent) and a small-royalty percentage on subsequent supplement sales (5 to 10 percent) you will use your expert status in the fitness and nutrition industry to author a book that introduces the world to the new product.

It's that simple. You will probably have to sign a non-disclosure agreement, and then the supplement company will provide you with the product information and research material. You write the book and give it to them in electronic format. Most supplement companies have access to dirt-inexpensive large-scale publishers, so you will incur no publishing costs. You just contribute your expert information and get paid, every time a bottle or a book sells—for years and years. Speaking of expert status in the supplement industry, the next chapter will tell you how to get there.

7

Nutrition

In this chapter, you'll learn about how to become educated and certified to dispense dietary advice, legal considerations of nutrition consulting, how to implement your offerings into a successful business, and one simple way to leverage your nutrition advice into a massive client-generating tool. I'll provide you with every website and tool that you need to have a smooth-running nutritional-consulting empire established within just a few weeks. Including nutrition services in your business can often generate greater revenue than the exercise component of personal training, and this chapter will teach you how.

Nutrition Consulting

Synergy is defined as the optimum balance of exercise, diet, and lifestyle choices that achieves ideal wellness. Can you truly provide synergy to your clients? It is incredibly difficult to bestow perfect synergy without the ability to share crucial diet and lifestyle information. Think of yourself as a wellness coach, and not just as an exercise trainer. You must be educated and certified in order to properly advertise your wellness services and share nutrition information.

Wellness and synergy make money. The shift away from westernized allopathic medicine into a more natural preventive approach has opened the door for a trillion dollar industry. I have clients who renew their incredibly expensive personal training memberships with me month after month, simply because I can provide them with wellness and synergy, while other less-certified trainers cannot.

Results make money. Without addressing both the exercise and nutritional components of total-body wellness, it is unlikely that you can successfully attain weight-loss results for your clients. You know for a fact that people can't exercise, eat whatever they want, and expect to lose weight. I have individuals come to me after working years with a drill sergeant-style personal trainer who does nothing but shout exercise orders. By gently nudging them in the direction of proper nutrition, I've achieved overnight results and produced very happy clients who tell all their friends.

I paid about $275 for my nutrition certification, and studied for it with a free book from the library, which I had one of my college interns pick up for me (the same book costs $90 through the certifying agency). Each day, I read an article from two or three different wellness newsletters, like www.mercola.com and www.whfoods.com, following the "one glance rule" (never look at the same piece of paper twice—read it once and move on). This method allows me to read the equivalent of two to three wellness books per month and provide frequently updated content to my clients.

In contrast, for about 10 minutes of reading every morning and a $275 certification, I net close to $2500 per week from my face-to-face nutrition-consulting services alone, and thousands more dollars through my established nutrition expert status and the leverage it provides for supplement sales, book sales, magazine and newspaper article writing, and public-speaking appearances. The certification paid for itself in about a half day of work, and the few minutes spent every morning reading net a few hundred dollars a day.

If you haven't yet tapped into the wealth of possessing a nutrition certification, then you're nowhere near your potential income as a trainer. Keep reading to find out how to reach that goal.

Certifications

If you have a CSCS or NSCA-CPT certification (www.nsca.com), or an exercise-science and health-related degree from a public institution, you are likely able to demonstrate the level of knowledge required to share basic nutritional information. Nationally recognized and respected certifications by the American College of Sports Medicine or National Academy of Sports Medicine may also allow you to disseminate such information.

However, if you just have a personal-training certification and want to really learn the ropes and establish yourself as an expert in the eyes of the public, you'll need a universally-recognized nutrition certification. When you read a nutrition article in a popular health or fitness magazine, you'll often notice that the author has the title "ISSN." This title means that they are certified by the International Society of Sports Nutrition. If you're moderately competent, you can start here and study for this exam for two to three months and be adequately prepared to pass. It is not an easy exam, but the process of learning the information and attaining the certification will truly make you stand out in the nutrition field. Visit the ISSN website for a list of certification dates and locations. If you work for a gym or corporation, you can usually convince them to pay your travel and registration fees for a certification. You just have to ask.

Once you have your certification, it is very important that you advertise your services using the correct definitions. You need to understand the distinct difference between a registered dietitian (RD) and a nutritionist. The American Dietetics Association defines an RD as a "food and nutrition expert who has met the minimum academic and professional requirements to qualify for the credential 'RD'."

An RD is a formally accredited, post-graduate college-attained degree that requires advanced-level college courses and large numbers of practical work experience, often in clinical environments working with individuals in a diseased state. Because I am not legally qualified to prescribe diet as medicine, I have a relationship with a local RD to whom I refer all my medically-challenged clients who need dietary management of medical conditions, and I would highly recommend you do the same. However, no legal definition exists for the term "nutritionist" and anyone, including the weekend home-study certification-style personal trainer, can refer to themselves as a nutritionist.

This concept works in reverse, however. Just because a person has an RD certification does not mean they know anything about fueling the body during exercise. I actually train and coach several RDs who are clueless about how to fuel and prepare their bodies for a marathon or triathlon. The RD to whom I refer clients for medically-related nutritional issues sends me clients for exercise-related nutritional issues. So, by attaining a sports-nutrition certification, you can fill a crucial gap, which is why you must attain an exercise nutrition certification that is well recognized and respected, and why I highly recommend the ISSN certification.

Legal Considerations

Welcome to the nasty, smelly can of worms in the personal-training industry. Can personal trainers legally and ethically dispense nutrition advice? For that matter, can "certified nutritionists" legally and ethically dispense nutrition advice? As a fitness professional, you are a gatekeeper of information on exercise and nutrition, but a great deal of disagreement exists over how you can actually share that information. Part of the disagreement is due to highly-differing state laws that govern nutrition practices, as well as a lack of consensus on the definition of diet prescription. To view state laws in more detail, visit www.super-super.com/nsca.

If your exercise-science college education was similar to mine, you may have been given the notion that all nutritional counseling, education, and recommendations should be performed by some type of college-educated nutrition professional. After all, that was the purpose of the college's nutritional department, right?

The fact is that current dietetics-licensure laws do not limit your right to provide nutrition advice and information, as long as that advice and information is not designed to manage a diagnosed medical condition. Aside from medical management (for example, a diet for diabetes), no clear consensus exists on when it is more appropriate to refer your client to a nutrition professional, such as a registered dietitian.

According to the American Dietetic Association's website, 44 states have statutory provisions regarding professional regulation of dietitians and/or nutritionists. But the definition of a dietitian or nutritionist is rarely clear, and many of the other definitions provided by state statutes are highly ambiguous.

For example, in Louisiana and Florida, a fitness professional is not allowed to ask what kind of foods a person eats, because this query could be defined as a nutritional assessment. And if the fitness professional discovers that the client is drinking 10 sodas per day, they are technically not allowed to recommend substituting sparkling water, because this advice may actually be defined as a dietary prescription.

But who is enforcing these statutes? And more importantly, what is the purpose of the statutes? To protect an individual from following uneducated advice, or to protect an individual from having to break their soft-drink habit?

In other words, I highly recommend advocating healthy lifestyle behaviors related to nutrition, whether it is to a client or to the person sitting beside you on the airplane. Unless you step way outside your boundaries and attempt to diagnose disease or treat medical conditions via diet, nobody is going to jump out from a closet and arrest you. Build a trust relationship with your clients, be very clear about what your nutrition certification or license actually is, and you will stay within legal boundaries.

For the best results, use the following tips:

- Provide general advice, not individualized and specific prescription. In other words, tell your clients that consuming low-glycemic index foods will stabilize blood sugar, and not that they need to consume lentils every day for lunch to lower their personal resting-insulin levels. Other good examples include: encouraging consumption of 6 to 10 small frequent meals throughout the day, eating natural, unprocessed foods, eating lean protein, unprocessed carbohydrates and healthy fat, and drinking water regularly.

- Suggest or highly recommend dietary supplements, but do not "prescribe" them. Tell the client that it is their choice, and recommend that they follow the manufacturer's instructions (don't write "take 3mg melatonin every night to help you sleep" on a piece of paper and hand it to your client), then put the ball in their court.

- Base all your advice on science and public information. If your client can't easily find research or information on a supplement or dietary protocol, you shouldn't be recommending it. For example, don't give your client the brand new weight-loss supplement that just arrived on the market, especially if it has no long-term studies and very little public information or history. Excellent peer-reviewed resources for finding well-researched information on diet supplements and nutrition include:
  - ✓ American Journal of Clinical Nutrition (www.ajcn.org/contents-by-date.0.shtml)
  - ✓ Consumer Labs® (www.consumerlab.com/tnp.asp)
  - ✓ Medline Plus (www.medlineplus.gov)
  - ✓ Natural Standard® (www.naturalstandard.com)
  - ✓ PubMed® (www.ncbi.nlm.nih.gov/sites/entrez)

✓ Reuters Health (www.reutershealth.com)
✓ WebMD® (www.webmd.com)

If you're very concerned about your legal liability, make it a habit to simply steer your clients in the right direction. One of my favorite websites for helping clients educate themselves on proper nutritional protocols is www.whfoods.com. A large number of websites, like www.fitday.com and www.caloriecounter.com, also exist that can help your clients track calories and take charge of their own diets. You can simply be the silent guide that stands by and nods them in the right direction.

Sharing Information

To establish your authority as an expert and keep clients coming back for more, you must provide knowledge empowerment. With information creation, you'll eventually be able to build a library of knowledge that makes your job easier, in the same way that creating libraries of workout templates allows you to quickly create exercise routines. Discuss nutrition frequently with your clients. While you cannot legally prescribe diets and tell people what they must eat, no rule exists that you cannot provide information to help address basic nutrition concerns. Examples of information-sharing documents that I use to save time and to educate clients are as follows:

- *18 Crucial Questions*. This 36-page diet document is distributed to all my weight-loss clients. It is a constantly evolving body of information on dietary techniques to lose weight. Containing glycemic-index tables, sample snack lists, vegetable-care techniques, and advice on choosing an energy bar, it is a document that not only saves me from fielding a million different questions, but will someday make a great e-book. Whenever I come across a compelling, but practical, piece of research, I add it to the document. When I sit down with a client for a nutritional consultation, I print the document, hand it to them, and use it as a template for our discussion. Usually, we get through about one third of the document, and then schedule another consultation to come back for more. All my clients keep a copy of this handout in their diet-log book.

- *Nutrition packet for endurance athletes*. This packet is a collection of information that tells personal anecdotes of my diet preparation for various Ironman triathlons, a sample race week carb-loading plan, a sample meal plan for endurance athletes, a list of recommended supplements and discount codes, and a constantly growing body of information that I add to whenever I come across an interesting endurance-related sport-nutrition topic. I simply write a brief one to two sentence explanation of the new information, and keep the packet up-to-date with about 10 minutes of work a month. This packet is distributed to all the athletes that I coach, and will also be sold as an e-book someday. Again, it saves me from having to answer a host of potential questions, especially as an athlete approaches an A-priority race. Why type the same e-mail over and over again to your athletes?

- *Sample meal plans*. Meal-plan templates are easy to create, and by creating and naming them as "sample" meal plans, you're making yourself less liable and not guilty of "dietary prescription," which you technically should not be doing (see the legal considerations section of this chapter). Figure 7-1 illustrates one type of meal plan template table that I use. I can use any type of recipe or meal that I drag and drop into the table. The particular meal plan shown in Figure 7-1 is for traveling. Notice that the plan includes options and choices. People love this factor. In the same way that I have dozens of different workout templates, I have sample meal-plan templates that are written on a daily, weekly, or monthly basis, for higher protein or higher carbohydrate-type diets, for weight loss, for endurance athletes, for power and strength athletes, for traveling, for fast food only—the list goes on. Once I create a meal plan for a particular client, I save it. With minor tweaking, it can be used over and over again. And yes, these will eventually be combined and sold as an e-book. Seeing a pattern?

- *Meal logs*. On my website, clients can download and print meal logs. Some people prefer to use this method, rather than going to Office Depot, Staples, or Barnes & Noble to buy a diary-type book. You'll want your clients to record a consistent set of variables. The most important are time, amount, proximity to workout, and appetite-based feelings. I also include a log with pre-populated answers so that clients can see exactly what I am looking for. For a sample meal log, refer to the combined diet and exercise log in Figure 3-4. And since a good diet requires fueling the body 6 to 10 times per day, I recommend more blank rows than those in the example.

- *Grocery-shopping lists*. These lists are great tools that can also be used in conjunction with the grocery-store marketing tip I will present later in this chapter. Grocery-shopping lists can easily be created for each of your sample meal plans by sifting through your recipes, selecting and copying each food, and pasting it into the grocery shopping list, which may seem like busy work, but if you do it once, you don't have to do it again, and these same grocery lists can be used in e-books.

Sample Meal Plan—Travel		
Meal	**Choice 1**	**Choice 2**
Breakfast	One piece fresh raw fruit: Apple, pear, grapefruit. Include one handful of nuts.	Clif Bar®, Hammer Bar®, BumbleBar, or Larabar. Not airplane or convenience store "granola" bar.
Airplane or car snack 1	Clif Bar, Hammer Bar, BumbleBar, or Larabar. Not airplane or convenience store "granola" bar.	One piece fresh raw fruit and cheese stick or a handful of walnuts, plus water.
Airplane or car snack 2	Snack vegetables: Sugar-snap peas, green beans, sliced peppers, olives, or celery, plus water.	One handful sunny seed or tropical mix and water. Not airplane snack mix. Tropical mix: equal parts walnuts, unsweetened coconut, unsweetened dried mango, unsweetened dried papaya, and brazil nuts
Airport or travel lunch	Wrap or sushi rolls: Choose a chicken, beef, or vegetable, whole grain, spinach, or lettuce wrap with no mayo, ranch, or Caesar. If sushi, choose brown rice version with no mayo.	Salad: Choose a salad that has the highest amount of vegetable variety and lowest amount of craisins®, croutons, snack mix toppings, etc. Use 1/2 to 1/4 packet of low-fat Caesar, ranch, or Italian dressing.
Dinner	Restaurant: Ethnic cuisine— Chinese, Indian, Thai, or other: order meat and vegetable dish, without rice or noodles. Italian: skip pasta, choose chicken, meat, or seafood with a vegetable side.	Grocery store or deli: Options— higher protein, lower carbohydrate deli salad, vegetable, or meat deli wrap, boiled egg, non-cream based deli soup, fruit, and nuts.
Additional Snack 1	Clif Bar, Hammer Bar, BumbleBar, or Larabar. Not airplane or convenience store "granola" bar.	Snack vegetables: Sugar-snap peas, green beans, sliced peppers, olives, or celery, plus water.
Additional Snack 2	Store-bought hummus (preferably from a health food store): Dip with celery, jikama, or sliced peppers.	One piece fresh raw fruit: Apple, pear, grapefruit, peach, etc. Include a handful of nuts.

Figure 7-1

Business Model

I provide nutrition services with a combination of both face-to-face consulting and an online presence. My fee-structure model and service descriptions are as follows:

- An online nutrition-coaching package

  Total access to a customized nutritional-advice program with Ben Greenfield, including a daily meal-plan suggestion and monthly meal calendar based on your personal goals, health history, schedule, and food likes/dislikes. The program includes e-mail access to Ben, 10-minute weekly phone consultations, nutritional logs, and detailed daily-diet instructions. This program emphasizes practical and achievable nutritional habits from a holistic perspective of total-body health, so you'll not only look good, but you'll feel great! No contract required—the cost is $500 per month.

  I also feature this package in combination with an online fitness-training package, for a total of $1000 per month. For this package, I also include a combination of three free e-books to seal the deal.

- A face-to-face nutritional consultation

  Meet with the top personal trainer in the nation, face-to-face at his office at Champions Sports Medicine in Spokane, Washington. Your consultation can cover any aspect of your lifestyle that you desire, including nutrition, goal setting, losing fat, gaining muscle mass, learning new exercises, or training-program design. If you want to learn an ideal nutritional plan, lose weight or gain muscle, avoid injury, get stronger or faster, and identify weaknesses in your training program, this meeting is for you. Each consultation includes a comprehensive written follow-up report that features personalized recommendations and feedback. You may repeat your one-time consultation during the year as desired. The cost is $200 per consultation.

- A phone consultation

  Features all elements of the face-to-face consultation, but offers a convenient Skype (www.skype.com) or phone option for individuals not in the Spokane/Coeur D'Alene area or who are unable to schedule a face-to-face session. The cost is $75 for 20 minutes.

Grocery Store Set-Up

In addition to magazine-article contribution, newspaper interviews, television appearances, and other marketing techniques discussed in Chapter 10, one powerful way exists to leverage your nutrition certification into generating a large number of clients.

- Dress professionally. Go to a grocery store near your house. Choose a clean, well-managed supermarket such as Rosauers, Albertsons, or Fred Meyers, as opposed to the corner mini-mart or 7-11. Ask to speak to the manager.

- Give the manager your business card. Explain that you are a nationally-certified nutrition and fitness professional with X years of expertise serving clientele in the local community. If possible, provide a sheet or brochure with testimonials and client references.

- Propose a method of boosting sales of the grocery store's higher priced "organic" and healthy foods (it is common knowledge among the grocery industry that these foods are harder to sell, due to their higher price tags). The method is: on a weekly or monthly basis, sometime between 9 am and 12 pm (when the "non-rushed" folks are shopping) you are going to set up a small table or booth near the entry doors and provide *free*, healthy sample meal plans and grocery lists, *free* nutrition and diet Q & As, and *free* nutritional label-interpretation assistance. The grocery store can feature coupons for health food at the table, and you can provide business cards or brochures for your personal-training and nutritional-consulting services.

This set-up is a win-win situation. The grocery store gives their shoppers the perk of a weekly or monthly certified expert guide on nutrition, and you gain the ability to meet an enormous number of clientele who actually want your advice. Eventually, if you present a professional and impressive presence, you can approach the manager about featuring you in the coupon newspaper ad, as the local diet superhero who stands smiling on the front page of the ad layout, prepared to come to your aid on any aisle.

I've thoroughly enjoyed this style of marketing, and even if you're at the grocery store for just one to two hours each month, it will pay big dividends. Remember—you want a client waitlist so that you can charge higher prices and *train for top dollar!*

8

Information Products

Imagine waking up in the morning, opening your computer, and finding out that you made a few hundred bucks while sleeping. Information-product creation is a huge component of fitness, and sharing your information virtually can reap enormous benefits. In this chapter, you'll learn how to easily create and market books, DVDs, and electronic information products, thus instantly automating your income. You'll learn how to find book agents and editors for successful publishing, how to replicate your DVDs and print your books both locally and nationally, and simple tips and tricks to get inexpensive UPCs, ISBNs, and bar codes. This chapter also includes specific instructions on one highly-effective strategy for taking all the headache out of finding a book agent and marketing your information product.

You are about to discover the wonderful world of information-product creation—a way to automate your income and make money while you sleep. Information products allow you to do as follows:

- *Instantly establish yourself as an expert in the fitness or nutrition topic of your choice.* If people recognize you as an author, they instantly associate your name with increased credibility. It doesn't matter if you know absolutely nothing about a topic—if you've written a book about it, you're an expert. This fact is an interesting phenomenon that I highly encourage you not to abuse. Once you've produced an information product, using the techniques described in this chapter, milk the credibility cow for all it's worth, including with every newspaper interview, press release, and online biography, the fact that you are the celebrated author of the best-selling book on X.

- *Automate your income and make money while you sleep.* Imagine that people visit your website from around the world and pay anywhere from $4.99 to $29.99 for your online-information products or physically-produced books and DVDs (for which you've outsourced publishing using the techniques presented in this chapter). Now, imagine that they're doing that while you sleep, eat, and shower. That's automated income.

- *Improve the bottom line in your direct sales.* Book and DVD products just give you one more item that you can sell, typically as a complementary feature to your nutritional-supplement line. Although I now outsource all my physical book and DVD replication, so that it is printed and reproduced in Taiwan, I always keep several copies on hand to sell to my clients. It is interesting that even when I am providing personal training to a client, they will purchase one of my books on diet and fitness just to keep on the coffee table and show their friends, who then want to sign up for training with a published author.

- *Gain search-engine optimization through book featuring on websites like Amazon®.* If your search-engine optimization isn't ideal, a potential customer or client may have a difficult time locating you in a top-10 Google search, but they're far less likely to have trouble finding you on the highly publicized Amazon website. Multiple ways exist to get your information product, electronic or otherwise, featured on Amazon.com®, which I'll explain later in this chapter.

• *Have a "free" product to attract people to sign up for your e-newsletter*. Rather than simply begging your website visitors to supply their name and e-mail address in exchange for an online-fitness or nutrition newsletter, try sweetening the deal a bit. Offer one of your e-books, valued at $59.99 (or whatever other random price you choose), but which is now included absolutely free for people who sign up for your newsletter. With a service like www.1shoppingcart.com, you can have your book automatically delivered to anyone who signs up for the newsletter. And automation is a good thing.

• *Possess a unique gift that you can give or sell to clients and potential customers*. I'll often use an information product as a bonus gift when a client signs up for their 12 months of membership, or as a special gesture for a potential customer when I need to close the deal ("throwing in" an e-book in a follow-up e-mail). Think of information products as a way to make your selling leverage just a little bit more powerful and your relationship with your current clients just a little bit stronger.

What Exactly is an Information Product?

Simply stated, an information product can be defined as: *a collection of information, digital or physical, that you package into a marketable product*. The information can be as simple as a list of sample menus that allow people to make intelligent nutrition decisions at popular franchised restaurants. Or it can be a comprehensive-exercise program with full-color exercise photos and detailed instructions. This book is an information product. The following list includes just a few of the other information products that I've produced and sell on a daily basis:

• *A collection of tips and tricks designed to speed up the metabolic rate and provide a brief overview of how the metabolic rate works*. I sell this book in physical form through CreateSpace® on Amazon.com (I'll explain later in this chapter), online in e-book format from various websites, and directly to clients. I have also used product leveraging on this book to feature specific metabolism-boosting supplements from a network-marketing company, who gives me free products in return (which I mark up and sell to my clients). I am currently setting up a relationship with an obesity-support and advocacy group, a charity to which I am going to donate a small percentage of book sales, whereby I will be able to market and sell this book to large fitness- and nutrition-related corporations, who can provide it to their consumers as a tax write-off. This book includes a short workout

DVD that I replicate locally in large volume and via CreateSpace DVD replication, and sell both separately and in combination with the book.

- *A three-week combined diet and exercise plan for quick weight loss*, which I sell in large volume to brides wanting to fit into a wedding dress, young men preparing for armed forces candidate-fitness assessments, and people who cannot afford personal training but will buy a combined diet and fitness book. The initial marketing launch of this book was achieved by contacting a local newspaper editor and offering to provide him with 24-7 personal-trainer support as he worked his way through the 21 days as a human-interest story. The story was published as a January 1st weight-loss piece and resulted in a massive number of book sales. Similar to the metabolism book, this book is sold in both e-book and physical format, and includes a comprehensive workout DVD.

- *An e-book/online video-combined product that presents a program for reducing low back pain in runners with rotated hips.* This information product is entirely digital, and includes links to high quality online videos of each exercise. Lower quality videos are available on YouTube, with descriptions and links that lead the viewer back to the product's website for purchase (a form of the viral video marketing that was presented in Chapter 4).

- *An e-book/online video-combined product that features several strength-training routines for endurance athletes.* I market this product via viral-video marketing, and also by contributing frequently to the highly popular forums of endurance websites like www.slowtwitch.com, where I make sure that a website featuring the book's URL appears in my signature. This strategy is also good to use for blog commenting.

- *A book on the habits of fat people* that is currently being produced by a major national publishing company who pays me royalties. This book was produced via an entirely different route—namely by producing a sample chapter, introduction, and book outline and forwarding to a book agent (a project that I've outsourced), who then found an editor from a publishing company who was interested in the project. I'll explain this technique later in this chapter.

- *A series of audio-information products*, which are available in a downloadable MP3 file that walks novice exercisers through a core-workout program. Each subsequent audio file gradually grows more difficult in exercises, sets, and reps.

How to Get Started

Identify Your Area of Expertise, Topic, and Niche Market

General exercise and diet books are a dime-a-dozen, so that's about all you'll be able to sell yours for—10 cents. But if you have an exercise and diet book that is designed for triathletes who need to carbohydrate load for the last week before Ironman, you've got a specific product and a good niche population (that just happens to be the thousands of athletes in one of the fastest growing sports on the planet). I make it a habit to discuss my forthcoming information products with my face-to-face clients to "test the waters" in terms of interest in the product. As would be expected, my most successful information products are the same products for which my clients showed the most interest.

Decide if You Want Your Product to be Digital or Physical

Both forms have their advantages and disadvantages. A digital product, such as a book or audio file, has zero overhead costs, zero printing costs, zero shipping and order fulfillment costs, zero physical storage-space requirements, and very low required maintenance. You typically can't charge quite as much for a digital product, however, and you cannot market it to the entire population that doesn't understand e-books, doesn't own a computer, or has no desire to own electronic-information content. Some people just don't trust the automatic-download process or find it a pain to print. Fortunately, in an electronic age, this population grows smaller every day. A copywriting issue also exists with digital-information products. It is very simple for someone to copy your digital-information product and send it to 10 of their friends, thus losing 10 customers for you, which is much more difficult to accomplish with a physical book (later in this chapter, I'll explain how you can protect your digital product with online-security functions).

Finally, a digital product is almost always self-published, which almost guarantees that if you ever decide to take the book public and attempt to market it in printed form through a publishing company, you probably won't be successful, as a jaded attitude exists toward previously self-published products. However, in my opinion and money-making experience, a digital product will ultimately pay larger dividends than a physical information product, unless you stumble upon a very attractive book deal with a major publishing company.

On the other hand, a physical information product, such as a book or DVD, is more expensive to design and print, difficult to store and warehouse, and much less convenient to create and self-publish. In the end, however, you'll be able to sell your product for a higher price to a broader demographic. You also have the option to find a literary agent or editor to represent your physical product to a publishing company (i.e., the "old-school" method of publishing). If your book or DVD hits it big, you can be an instant celebrity and receive higher paying royalty that exceeds the revenue from a digital product. Physical products are also easy to keep around your office, gym, or studio for direct sales to customers and clients.

Produce Your Content

I will discuss specifics of digital vs. physical product creation in the next section. Regardless of which method you choose, you must actually take the good ideas circulating through your brain and put those ideas onto paper or into digital format. Unless you have a very small product, you should create your content in small and manageable chunks. In the span of three concentrated hours, I've written an 18 page e-book that has so far sold over 200 copies at $19.95, which means I made over $1300 per hour. However, I've made much more money from the books for which I've worked a little harder, where I create an actual book outline with chapter titles and sub-topics, using a simple bulleted Word-document format, which takes anywhere from 30 minutes to two hours, depending on the book size. I then "fill in the blanks," expanding on the chapter content on an hourly or daily basis. Using this method, and giving myself one hour each day, I can produce a chapter every three days, which means a 10-chapter book takes about a month (exactly the length of time it took to create *Personal Trainers' Guide to Earning Top Dollar*). For example, Chapter 9 was outlined as shown in Figure 8-1. (Note: A chapter typically evolves as I fill in the outline, so the finished Chapter 9 may appear much different.)

Title chapter: Offsite Training

- Why train offsite?
  - ✓ Advantage/disadvantages
  - ✓ Liabilities/waivers
- Corporate model
  - ✓ Sample service and fee schedule
  - ✓ Corporate-wellness program/gym design
  - ✓ Seminars
  - ✓ Executive health
- Home model
  - ✓ Sample service and fee schedule
  - ✓ Gym design
  - ✓ Home meetings

Figure 8-1

The plan of attack that is illustrated in Figure 8-1 works quite well for digital-information products and physical-information products that are self-published, but if you plan on creating a book and are attempting to hook up with a literary agent or editor, a far less time-consuming and more intelligent plan of action exists. Although you'll still be able to use the aforementioned chapter-outlining method, you probably aren't going to want to produce your entire physical book content (because this step could be a waste of your time if it isn't actually published). The next section discusses my recommended approach to this dilemma.

Physical Information Products

Accordingly, you decide your information product is going to be a physical book, you don't want the hassle of self-publishing, and you want to be picked up by a publishing company. You have your title, you have your ideas, you have your chapter outlines, and you have an idea of your intended market. The next step is—*you'll need an agent*.

The process of finding a literary agent can be one of the most frustrating steps in getting a book published, and one of the most important. I choose to outsource part of this process, which I'll explain later in this section. Unless you have a very good friend who works for a publishing company, an agent will be necessary to get your book (or as I'd recommend, your book query) into the hands of a receptive editor, who will decide if your book has what it takes. At this point, you need to take the following steps:

- *Produce sample content before contacting literary agents*. Proofread and perfect your sample content. I recommend preparing a book introduction (typically two to five pages in length), a table of contents with the title of each chapter and a brief single sentence overview of each chapter, one *completed* sample chapter, an author biography, and an introductory letter to the agent (which when packaged with your content is officially called a "book query"). Entire books exist that are devoted to the process of creating a perfect book query. I own several and I recommend picking one up from your local library or bookstore.

- *Establish credibility*. Don't even try to get your book published unless you've already created articles in magazines and newspapers or been featured in some sort of public space as a speaker or writer. Include references to these credibility-creating activities in your query or author biography.

- *Research literary agents*. Find out who represents authors that produce similar content to yours. You don't want an agent that represents books on the floral industry if you're writing a manual for preparing for boot camp. An excellent book is *Guide to Literary Agents*. You can also subscribe to www.publishersmarketplace.com

an industry newsletter that announces deals and offers fee-based access to an online database of agents and editors. Create a list of agents who fall into the category of individuals who have represented books similar to yours. Avoid any agents that charge "reading fees," as it is typically a scam.

- *Submit your content to the agent.* Send via e-mail or postal mail your entire book query (you'll have to find out which format the agent prefers). It is acceptable to submit to multiple agents simultaneously, as long as you inform the agent in your query letter. In your research, you may find that all an agent desires is a one-page query letter. In this case, don't knock the agent out with your sample chapter, book outline, etc., as he will probably toss it in the trash. Enclose a self-addressed stamped envelope if you send your query via postal mail.

- *Sit back and wait.* It is acceptable after two weeks to inquire whether an agent received your information. Be prepared to do some revision, don't take rejection personally, and be willing to try multiple agents before achieving success. This process is time-consuming, which is why I outsource part of the process, namely the agent-research component, using www.elance.com or www.odesk.com. Figure 8-2 details a sample project that I posted.

Two days after posting the project, I had a complete list of agents on my desk in Excel-spreadsheet format, complete with mailing addresses and contact information. This posting only cost $150, and probably would have taken me 10 to 12 hours to do myself.

As you can see, this step is just the beginning of having your book picked up by a major publishing company, or any publisher for that matter. While it may net a little less money, if this is your first venture into information-product creation and you want to create a physical product, the self-publishing route for physical book or DVD creation can be a bit less intimidating.

Perhaps you want complete control of the project, from book printing or DVD replication with a local company, to product storage in your garage or studio, to order fulfillment using a FedEx® business account. I've outlined the steps for producing and selling your self-published physical content using the printing and DVD replication services in your local community. I used examples from the first book that I produced locally, which is a simple three-week diet and exercise plan with an accompanied workout DVD.

Complete your project in the correct format for a third party publisher or replicator.

For books, this step means you must personally have the book completely designed, or hire a graphic designer to design the layout for you. For my business, I spent $300

Sample Online Outsourcing-Project Proposal

What I need done:

I need you to develop a complete list of literary agents who may potentially be able to represent my book entitled "XXX X XX XXX." Ideally, I would like to have information on 10 to 30 agents, in Word document or Excel-spreadsheet format. After receiving this information from you, I will then be contacting these agents to represent a non-fiction book about weight loss, nutrition, fitness, and a healthy lifestyle. I do not need you to contact the agents; I just need all the agent information.

Required agent qualifications:

- Must have been in business for at least two years
- Must belong to the Association of Author's Representatives
- Must prefer books that cover the following topics: weight loss, diet, nutrition, health, fitness, exercise, and/or wellness
- Must not charge a "reading" or "editing" fee

Required agent information:

- Name (first, last), company, title, e-mail, phone 1, phone 2, website address 1, address 2, city, state, zip, notes (Please enter any notes on card, or information that does not fit into the fields above.)
- How the agent prefers to receive book queries, whether via e-mail, postal mail, or website submission, and whether a self-addressed stamped envelope is required
- Specific instructions on submission guidelines for a book query, including whether an agent requires sample chapters or other materials. I need to know the agent's exact stated guidelines.
- Complete agent biography, if available
- Agent's fees and commissions, if available
- Complete list of the agent's books that he has previously represented, listed by title and publisher
- List of author qualifications looked for by the agent, if available

Timeframe for project delivery:

As soon as possible. My book query is complete and ready to be sent. You may read complete information on how to search for an agent safely at http://www.sff.net/people/VictoriaStrauss/agentsearch.html.

I will award a project to an acceptable bidder within two days of selection.

Figure 8-2

on the Adobe Suite, a collection of software programs that allows me to create high-quality PDF documents and use a host of book templates and designs that are already included in the software suite. I write the book in Microsoft Word, then copy and paste the entire book into a pre-set Adobe InDesign® book template that automatically arranges page layout in a format that typically needs only minor tweaking to be ready for my local printing company. If you don't own your own software, plan on hiring a local graphic designer or via www.elance.com or www.odesk.com to properly design and size your book.

Make sure you know the actual size and format that you desire. The first time I self-published locally, I opened the Yellow Pages and called eight different local printing services. For each printer, I told them my approximate number of pages and asked for a list of pricing for color vs. black and white. I also asked for pricing on various book sizes (like 8.5x11, 5x7, and 4.5x6). If you have an idea of a book that is similar to your idea of a good size for your book, go to Barnes & Noble, or any other bookstore, with your tape measure and measure the book dimensions (or just look for the book on Amazon.com).

DVDs are much simpler to format and size for publishing, as they typically are produced in only a few standard small or large jewel cases. Assuming that you've already followed the tips in Chapter 3 for video collection and editing, it is very simple to export to a DVD format that you can burn onto a physical disc in your personal computer's read/write drive using Windows Movie Maker for a PC or iMovie/iDVD® for a Mac.

For my first locally produced DVD, I used a template that the local DVD replication studio had on their computer. I simply gave them the artwork cover for the actual book that I was publishing along with the DVD, and they turned it from a square into a nice circular shape that fit perfectly on a disc. This service was free. If you have the Adobe Suite software, or any decent graphic-design software, you can create your DVD cover yourself. Download a free template from www.proactionmedia.com, or any other online DVD-replication service, and then design your cover so that it fits that particular template size. For local production packaging, I simply opted for the free disc sleeves that were included with my DVD replication at the local studio (although I could have stepped up to the plastic jewel cases for an extra 20 cents per DVD). If you want a full-size case similar to a movie case or a package capable of carrying a multiple DVD set, you will probably have to outsource your DVD replication to an online-replication service, which I'll discuss later in this chapter.

Obtain an ISBN or UPC code, and copyright if desired.

RR Bowker is the official agency in the United States that assigns an ISBN, or International Standard Book Number, to each book title (DVDs get UPC codes). You can purchase one ISBN for $125, or, if you plan to publish more than one product, a block of 10 ISBNs for $235. Unfortunately, RR Bowker makes things difficult for self-publishers with an application page that suggests you need to buy a minimum block of 10 ISBNs, when you only need to purchase one. To purchase just one ISBN, call RR Bowker at 877-310-7333 and select option #4 in the voicemail. Ask them to fax you an application to apply for just one ISBN. Otherwise, to apply via the traditional method for 10 ISBNs, visit www.isbn.org/standards/home/isbn/us/secureapp.asp.

If you're selling a DVD, you must become a member of the UCC (Uniform Code Council). You have to register online as a company and you are issued a company number, which becomes a part of your UPC codes. The cost is $750 for a block of 100 codes, plus an annual renewal fee of $150, which is expensive. Therefore, I recommend buying a UPC code from a reseller for about $89 from Rovix at www.upccode.net, or, if you have a membership, for about $35 from www.buyabarcode.com. You can even get a single UPC code for $10 from www.indieartistalliance.com. If you use one of the online disc-replication services discussed later in this chapter, you won't even need to buy a UPC, and in my opinion, this approach is the way to go. When you have your ISBN or UPC, you'll also need a scannable bar code of it that has to appear somewhere on the book or DVD, so that it can be sold and tracked by vendors. The bar code must match the ISBN or UPC number. You can purchase bar codes for books from Bowker at www.isbn.org (for $25 per bar code) at the same time that you are applying for ISBNs. A company called Bar Code Graphics will generate bar codes from both ISBN and UPC at $10 per code. You'll receive the bar code via e-mail as a graphic file, and you can then paste it into your book or DVD cover artwork and send it to your graphic designer. If your book is already printed, just print your bar codes on labels and stick them on the back cover.

Finally, copywriting is an option. For all information on copywriting (which, in my opinion, is often not worth the hassle or fee), visit http://www.copyright.gov/. Copywriting only has to be set up if you plan on wanting to take legal action against someone for reproducing your content.

After properly sizing your product and obtaining an ISBN or UPC code, find a local company to print your book or replicate your DVD.

Prior to publishing my books locally, I had already decided on a printing company based on the pricing I received for the size and format. The first local publishing job was for a color-cover book with a black and white interior (a format that I highly recommend) at 120 pages. A color-cover book with a color interior was far more expensive. You can choose if you want the book perfect-bound, coil-bound, hardcover, softcover—the list and the pricing are infinite. Typically, perfect-bound, softcover is the most economical

For a slightly more expensive coil-bound format, which I chose for my first locally-produced book, I paid about seven dollars per copy. I ordered a "test market" volume of 100 books for a little over $700. Along the same time interval, I found a local DVD-replication studio by looking under the listing "video services" in my local yellow page directory. They replicated 200 DVDs from the DVD that I burned in my personal computer, and labeled and packaged each DVD into sleeves for three dollars each. I printed twice as many DVDs as books so that I could sell the DVDs separately to people who did not want to pay for the book, but could afford a less expensive workout DVD.

When my book had been proofed, accepted by me, and was finished printing (expect this entire process to take about two weeks), I brought the DVDs to the book-printing company and convinced them to shrink-wrap the books with the DVDs on the back cover of the book. As a favor, they did this for free (but I highly recommend negotiating favors like this *before* the sale). For the second printing of the book, I just bought double-sided sticky tabs at a local fabric store and had an intern slap each DVD onto the inside back cover of the book.

Now that your books and/or DVDs are ready, distribute your information product locally.

Armed with my boxes of book/DVD packages, I personally approached the owner of every local gym and nutrition-outlet store over the span of two weeks. I gave each owner one sample copy of my book for free to share with staff and keep for customers at the front desk. I also gave the owner five sealed copies of my book and a signed agreement to sell each package for $29.95 and keep 25 percent of the profit. In this agreement, I included a very important phrase that the gym was personally responsible for all five copies. Accordingly, if any copies should disappear unaccounted for, the gym would still need to pay me 25% of the listed price per book, which meant with my $10 cost per package, I would net $12 per sale, and the gym or nutrition-supplement outlet would spend nothing upfront.

I chose this particular method, rather than selling the companies the actual books, because I wanted to see how the test printing of the packages fared before attempting to intensively market them. Also, I had to get the packages out to the public without much resistance from my distributors.

At my personal gym, through my direct sales online, and at Amazon.com, I sold the packages for $22.95, making the same amount per book, but gaining the ability to offer my package at a lower price. This factor was important because it allowed me to test the success of two different prices, and to advertise to my online customers that they could receive a lower "Internet-only" price. You'd be amazed at the number of individuals who see a product at a store, then go home to research a lower price online. At the end of one month, I called each gym and ascertained sales progress. Accounting for the free products that I gave away, I profited $1056 from this local book/DVD package-selling process, which netted a profit of $10.56 per book.

This process was absolutely worth all the trouble, because even though I only made a little over $1,000 for what amounted to nearly 40 hours of book creation, labor, driving, and delivery (thus only making $25 per hr), I was instantly established as the local expert in diet and fitness, confirming the fact that people place automatic trust in a published (or self-published) author. I had a powerful marketing tool to add to my biography, my sales letters, my consultations, and my website. I still had both of these books in e-book, PDF format for further electronic marketing and if I didn't feel like actually printing more books, I could sell online or distribute to my clients in CD form.

I was a listed author at Amazon.com (very easy to do, and very simple-to-follow instructions at www.amazon.com). With my Amazon account, I was also given a FedEx business-shipping account for a huge discount on shipping of the books that I sold online. Interestingly, I also had a large number of clients approach me from all the local gyms that had featured my book. They bought the book, and now they wanted the trainer.

Now I outsource this entire time-consuming physical information product-creation process using an amazing tool called CreateSpace®, an Amazon affiliate at www.createspace.com. After I've created and designed the book and DVD, the entire process—book and DVD printing, order fulfillment, marketing, and shipping—is completely outsourced. I make less money per book, but have far more time. And time is money.

CreateSpace

CreateSpace is an online affiliate of Amazon that is a third party print-on-demand service for physical (and digital) information products. Using book templates, DVD cover templates, and standardized forms and instructions from www.createspace.com, you create your book and upload it in digital format to the CreateSpace website (or send your completed DVD in the mail). They then print your book or produce your labeled DVD, package it in your desired format, and send you a proof in the mail.

Upon receiving the proof, you log into your CreateSpace account and accept or revise the design. CreateSpace then lists your book and DVD on a variety of websites (most importantly Amazon.com); prints and ships your book or DVD when a customer places an order; and offers you wholesale prices on your creations, so that you can purchase them and sell to your local consumers.

From your CreateSpace member account, you can update and edit your title information, information-product description, artwork, sales channels, and sales reports. All books are produced as perfect-bound, paperback books with full-color covers, and you can choose to have a black and white or full-color interior. For DVDs, you have the option of multi-disc sets, multi-case collections, and combined sets (both CDs and DVDs in one case). Conveniently, you do not need to purchase an ISBN or UPC for a book or DVD submitted to CreateSpace. For no charge, ISBNs and UPCs are automatically assigned to your books and DVDs.

CreateSpace will pay you royalty on your sales at the end of each month, and takes complete care of sales collections, customer returns, and payment processing. You can opt to have your payments directly deposited into your bank account. Also, all books published through CreateSpace are eligible for the Search Inside! feature at Amazon, and digital products uploaded to CreateSpace are available for sale at www.mobipocket.com and Amazon's digital-text platform Kindle®, which offers a seamless and convenient method of making your physical-information products available digitally to a large customer population.

For other information-product services with print-on-demand services similar to CreateSpace, try www.lulu.com and www.booksurge.com, which have similar options. For other online DVD replication services that will inexpensively produce your DVD, assign and affix a UPC and bar code, then ship your DVDs to you or wherever you need them warehoused, try www.proactionmedia.com or www.discmakers.com.

Digital Information Products

Conveniently, after reading the section on physical information-product creation, you know most of what you need to know to actually create and design your content. The only difference between digital- and physical-information products is that the digital product is not printed or replicated. It is simply sent in electronic format to your customer, thus saving you hours of time and labor that you would normally spend on physical-product creation. E-books and audio-information products are the most popular forms of digital information.

Heed my warning: you can't just create your e-book, export it in .pdf format, make it available for digital download via your online shopping-cart system, and expect it to sell. Take note of these simple steps to creating your digital information products for effective selling.

- *Design your product*. Appearance is everything. People do judge a book by its cover. Your e-book, audio product, or video must be properly packaged or people will not buy it. Have you ever seen a website that features e-books, audio CDs, or video DVDs that look like the real thing but are actually only available in digital format? That effect is accomplished via a clever technique using simple software. You can take a raw graphic file of your e-book or audio information "cover logo," and easily tweak it into an impressive three-dimensional design that looks like a real book or DVD.

- ✓ For e-book cover design, go to www.killercovers.com.
- ✓ For e-book cover software, go to www.professionalecovertemplates.com.
- ✓ If you have the Adobe Suite and want superior e-book cover software, go to www.coveractionpro.com.
- ✓ If you don't use Adobe Suite's templates, get templates for the actual interior design of your e-book at www.ebookgraphics.com.
- ✓ If you don't want any hassle at all, hire a designer at www.e-lance.com or www.odesk.com to do it for you, usually for about $80 to $100.

- *Format your product*. For your e-books, you must convert your Word documents or text files into the standard e-book format, which is a PDF document. If you have the Adobe suite mentioned earlier in this chapter, you're set, and all customers will require to view your information product is the free Adobe reader available at www.adobe.com. Another good way to create your PDF is by using the free trial download of PDF creator software at http://www.pdf-creator.net/. All you need to do is select "print," then choose Adobe PDF as your output format. For your audio products, such as podcasts, you'll need to convert them to digital files like .wav or .mp3 using the techniques described in Chapter 3, then burn them to CD, or upload the files to your website or shopping-cart system.

- *Protect your product*. This step is up to you, depending on how highly you value your digital information product. As mentioned earlier, compared to a physical product, it is far easier to pirate and distribute a digital product. Your content can easily be ripped off.

I have protected my content using three different methods. The last is the most effective, but also the most expensive: one, use the Adobe Suite software to automatically assign a password to your e-book that is e-mailed, preferably in an automated fashion, to each client (only applicable to e-books, and only allows for one password, which can easily be leaked to the public); two, use eBook Pro at www.ebookpro.com to design and password protect your book; and three, use the convenient digital-product username and password function from www.1shoppingcart.com, which will assign a unique username and password for each product sold.

On the other hand, you can opt not to protect your product. If you've included links to affiliates throughout your e-book, then technically, a wider distribution of that product may net you money. Or if you've referenced your books and DVDs or personal training services in an audio-information product, you may find that sales improve as your priced audio product makes its way onto a free download page.

- *Sell your product.* If you're just getting started and anticipate a small sales volume, just put a link to your product on your website, use a simple sales button from Google Checkout or PayPal, and physically e-mail your book to a customer when they make a purchase. This system may be manageable for just 5 to 10 sold products per day, but if you plan on selling hundreds per week, it will eventually be a full time job. I highly recommend using the www.1shoppingcart.com automated digital-delivery system for your digital-product sales. The customer presses purchase, the product automatically downloads to their computer, the program automatically sends e-mail instructions with a link to the product (in case your customer missed the download page), and the product is also password protected if you've opted into that feature. It's as simple as that!

You've just finished reading what is, in my opinion, the most valuable chapter in this book. Information-product creation will take you to the next level and allow you to command your paycheck. The possibilities are endless, especially for digital-information products, and by learning the process you will set yourself up to take financial advantage of the shift toward electronic-information sharing as the gold standard in the next decade. On the other hand, if you desire, you can simply print a small batch of books, establish yourself as the local expert, and have a client waitlist for life!

9

Off-Site Training

Home and corporate personal training offers opportunity for zero overhead costs, a much higher paying clientele, and a larger number of potential customers. This chapter teaches you how to build your off-site training business using corporate seminars and wellness programs and home and corporate personal-training gym-design consultation. You'll learn how to net thousands of dollars per month from wealthy home clients and corporate groups, while receiving compensation for driving time and gas costs—with zero overhead fees. This chapter also includes several highly effective strategies for fee structure and marketing.

Why Train Off-Site?

Off-site training takes you outside the zone of your personal training studio or gym, and puts you into the personal environment of your clients. In my business, I personally take advantage of two off-site training situations: the corporate environment and the home environment. I also include several twists on each situation that I present in this chapter. There are distinct advantages and disadvantages to off-site training.

Advantages

Overhead costs for off-site training are close to zero, since your clients are spending the money on lighting, heating, and gym space. There is no check-in computer, no office manager, no secretary to greet your clients, and no lease. Equipment replacement and maintenance costs are not your responsibility. A home can be more comfortable than your office and often a client will feed you and give you random gifts that they no longer want (I've received many free lunches and random bicycles, medical equipment, and pieces of furniture). If you're charging what you should be charging, most of your home clients will be very wealthy, which can make your time at their home quite pleasant. Similarly, because of a large cash flow, a corporate space can have many more perks than your training studio, and most of my corporate customers have access to state-of-the-art training equipment and very posh gyms with perfect air conditioning and HD televisions. Because they are in their own environment, home and corporate clients typically train at far more flexible hours than traditional clients. Most importantly, the price that you charge can significantly increase, since one, off-site training is typically considered a concierge service, and two, you'll have more access to groups of individuals to train, such as families and corporate groups.

Disadvantages

In off-site training, you must travel and spend more time per session. Depending on where you live, off-site training can involve driving for five minutes to a full hour. I was in college when I made my first attempt at home training. I scheduled the session and agreed to come to the client's home for $25 more than what I typically charge. It took me 40 minutes to find the house on a back-country road, another five minutes to make my way through the client's home and into their gym, 10 minutes to familiarize myself with their gym equipment, 45 minutes of actual exercise, then 10 minutes to finally get out of the house (believe it or not, it's actually harder to leave a home than to kick a client out of your gym or office), and another 25 minutes to get home. This scenario did not account for money spent on gas, and the fact that I couldn't train a client in the hour immediately before or after the home client.

You also have higher liability. It is important to understand that anytime you step outside of your gym, you are no longer covered by the gym's insurance policy, so you must carry your own personal-liability insurance when training off-site. If you run your own studio, you already have this coverage and it will protect you anywhere (although you should check to make sure). If you work for a gym, you must purchase more insurance for yourself.

This chapter will give the details of fee structure for both home and corporate off-site training, and also include tips and tricks for making the process as seamless, convenient, and high-paying as possible.

Liability

First, I'd like to discuss the important part, which is liability. Figure 9-1 shows a sample of a waiver very similar to the one that all my home clients must sign. All my corporate clients must sign a waiver, and in addition, a representative of a corporation itself must sign a waiver. I tweak this waiver as necessary, depending on the specific situation.

Keep your signed waivers in a secure location, preferably in a locked folder in your home or office, or scan them and keep them in electronic format in a password-protected folder on your computer. Now that you've covered yourself legally, I would like to examine how to structure your personal training.

Home Personal Training

It is important to understand that when you perform a home personal-training session, you are doing your clients a "favor." Your clients are at home, wearing whatever they want, they don't have to drive anywhere, they get to eat a pre- and post-workout meal straight from the refrigerator or pantry, they can answer their phones or check their e-mail messages as they please, and they can brag to their neighbors that *their trainer comes to them*—a marketing tool that I utilize successfully, using my geographic model of home training, which cuts down costs and involved time. This model involves the following method:

Sample Waiver for Off-Site Training

Please read the following waiver, then, if you agree to the terms, sign your name.

Activity: Any and all prescribed, instructed, or suggested activities from Pacific Elite Fitness, LLC, including outdoor-endurance running and sprinting, running, jogging, and walking at a moderate to high effort on a grass surface; muscular stretching and flexibility exercises; body weight and calisthenic exercises, including push-ups, sit-ups, squats, and lunges; plyometric and jumping activities, including straight-up and side-to-side jumping on a surface, such as rubber, grass, and asphalt; suggested take-home exercises; open-water swimming (for triathletes and swim lessons), often at depths above head level; weightlifting; rowing; stairclimbing; indoor bicycling; bicycling on and off roads that are open to traffic; dismounting from bicycle; tracking nutritional intake; increasing or decreasing caloric intake; suggested meal plans, menus, or recipes; food supplementation; or any other activity prescribed, instructed or suggested from Pacific Elite Fitness, LLC and not listed in this document.

Release of Claims, Assumption of Risk, Contact, and Waiver of Liability

I understand and am aware that this activity is potentially hazardous. I acknowledge the possibility that injuries and physical and mental changes arising during and/or resulting from engaging in this activity do exist. These injuries and changes include, but are not limited to, abnormal blood pressure, fainting, disorders in heartbeat, heart attack, joint injuries, and, in some instances, death. I understand injuries and changes could result in my becoming partially or totally disabled and incapable of performing any gainful employment or having a normal social life.

I am voluntarily participating in this activity with knowledge of the dangers involved. I understand and take sole responsibility for any and all injuries and changes that may occur to myself and/or others, including but not limited to Pacific Elite Fitness, LLC, related to any and all activities associated with Pacific Elite Fitness, LLC, even if not specifically set forth in this document, whether or not they fall within the scope of reasonably foreseeable injuries related to this activity, and whether or not undertaken in the presence of staff or physical location of Pacific Elite Fitness, LLC. Although Pacific Elite Fitness, LLC will take precautions to ensure my safety, I expressly assume and accept sole responsibility for my safety and for any and all injuries and changes that may occur.

I release Pacific Elite Fitness, LLC from any and all liability for any personal injury, death, property damage or loss I may suffer as a result of my participation in this activity, and for any cause whatsoever, including negligence on the part of Pacific Elite Fitness, LLC.

I declare myself physically and mentally sound and suffering from no condition, impairment, disease, infirmity, or other illness that would prevent my participation in this activity. I acknowledge I have been informed of the need of a physician's approval for my participation in an exercise/fitness activity. I recognize it is my sole responsibility to obtain an examination by a physician prior to involvement in any exercise program. I acknowledge I have either had a physical examination and been given my physician's permission to participate, or if I have chosen not to obtain a physician's permission prior to beginning this activity, I acknowledge I am doing so at my own risk.

I understand that if, under any circumstances, I experience lightheadedness, dizziness, muscular pain, excessive fatigue, or any other painful or uncomfortable signs that exceed normal exercise fatigue, that I am not obligated to continue this activity. Furthermore, I may stop this activity at any time as I desire.

Pacific Elite Fitness, LLC employs certified-personal trainers, not physicians or registered dieticians. Pacific Elite Fitness, LLC does not diagnose or treat disease. I have been informed that I should consult a physician

Figure 9-1

before undergoing any dietary- or food-supplement changes. Any recommendations or suggestions from Pacific Elite Fitness, LLC for changes in my diet, including, but not limited to, the use of food supplements, food substitutions, caloric intake, meal plans, recipes, and menus are entirely my responsibility, and I release Pacific Elite Fitness, LLC from any and all liability for any illness, personal injury, death, property damage, or loss I may suffer as a result of any change in my nutrition, diet, or food intake.

I acknowledge and agree that no warranties or representations have been made to me regarding the results I will achieve from this program. I understand that the results are individual and may vary.

I understand that I have paid or am obligated to pay Pacific Elite Fitness, LLC a negotiated fee for this activity, and that under no circumstances is any of this amount refundable. I agree to commit to training with Pacific Elite Fitness, LLC for _____ (months/years) and agree to pay Pacific Elite Fitness, LLC a fee of _____ per (week/month/year) for my participation in this activity. In order to not be charged for a meeting, I understand that I am required to give 24 hours notice of cancellation for any meeting with a representative of Pacific Elite Fitness, LLC. If I decide not to engage in a training program, I agree to pay a consultation fee of $85 for my initial meeting with a representative from Pacific Elite Fitness, LLC.

I give Pacific Elite Fitness, LLC permission to use my name, likeness, image, voice, written words, and/or appearance as may be embodied in any pictures, photos, video recordings, audiotapes, digital images, written documents, and the like, taken or made on behalf of Pacific Elite Fitness, LLC activities. I agree that Pacific Elite Fitness, LLC has complete ownership of such pictures, etc., including the entire copyright, and may use them for any purpose. These uses include, but are not limited to, illustrations, bulletins, exhibitions, videotapes, reprints, reproductions, publications, advertisements, and any promotional or educational materials in any medium now known or later developed, including the Internet. I acknowledge that I will not receive any compensation, etc. for the use of such pictures, etc., and hereby release Pacific Elite Fitness, LLC and its agents and assigns from any and all claims which arise out of or are in any way connected with such use. I understand that if I desire this information to remain private and not be publicly used by Pacific Elite Fitness, LLC, I may express this desire in written format at any time prior to beginning this activity.

I acknowledge I have thoroughly read this waiver and release and fully understand it is a waiver and release of liability. By signing this document, I am waiving any right I, or my heirs and/or assigns, may have to bring any and all legal actions or assert any and all claims against Pacific Elite Fitness, LLC, its respective representatives, executors, and/or assigns. I confirm that I have read over this agreement before signing, that I understand it, and that it will be binding not only on me but also on my heirs, my next of kin, my executors, administrators, and assigns.

I represent and warrant I am signing this agreement freely and willfully and not under fraud or duress. I further represent and warrant no social relationship exists between Pacific Elite Fitness, LLC and me, or if such a social relationship exists, for purposes of my training sessions, trainer and I have assumed a strict business relationship, and I understand any social relationship does not render this waiver invalid. These exculpatory clauses are intended to apply to any and all activities occurring during the time for which I have contracted with Pacific Elite Fitness, LLC.

_____
Participant's name (please print clearly)

_____   Date: _____
Participant's signature

_____   Date: _____
Parent/guardian signature (if applicable)

_____   Date: _____
Pacific Elite Fitness, LLC staff signature

Figure 9-1 (cont.)

Batch your home personal-training sessions to a specific geographic section of your town or metropolitan area. Because you will be charging high prices for your services, most likely you will only be providing home training to wealthy clients. In every situation, I've found that in rich neighborhoods, word spreads quickly to neighbors. When I ran a successful home personal-training business, I only trained in three different very wealthy sections of town—one on Monday mornings, one on Thursdays, and one on Friday. The Monday mornings were at two homes, with one individual at one home and a family of three at another home, which was one mile away. The Thursday and Friday sessions were at four to five homes that were within three blocks of each other. I devoted one hour to each session, and this hour included driving time.

A home personal-training session is structured very similarly to a face-to-face session at your gym or studio, although you're using your client's equipment and may have limitations based on what is available. Accordingly, I train some clients at home with nothing more than a yoga mat and a stability ball. Other clients have 1000- to 2000-square-foot personal home gyms that rival an upscale health club.

Another difference between a home session and a gym session is that you can charge a much higher fee for home training. See Figure 1-1 for a detailed home personal training fee schedule. I recommend that in addition to the fees listed, you also include a travel stipend for yourself. In my business, that stipend has ranged from $15 to $30 per session, depending on driving time. Remember that if your state charges a business tax on your services, you will have to add tax to these prices.

Each additional person, if training during the same hour as the first person, receives a 50% discount (i.e., the wife trains at $400, and the husband and one child train at $200 per person). As you can see, this type of group-training scenario nets me $800 per month for four hours of home training, with all driving and gas costs covered.

In addition to the normal face-to-face sessions, *I charge my home personal training clients for travel time and gas costs*, using the following strategy: I determine the amount I am charging the client per minute, and multiply this value by the number of minutes I spend traveling to and from the client's home. This factor usually adds $10 to $20 per session, which I include on my client's invoice or automatically charge to his credit card. Gas mileage is determined by the number of miles and per gallon cost of gas. I am very upfront with these particular costs and have never encountered resistance.

I advertised these services on my website and in a single page brochure as being available in a limited geographic area, and turned down any clients that required me to drive more than 20 minutes, because I personally do not like to drive. I also included the advertisement as a single-page feature on the bulletin board of every golf course within 10 minutes of my home, which is a very effective strategy for catching the eye of the type of demographic who purchases home training. When initially attempting to establish a home personal-training client base, I included the following line at the bottom of the advertisement:

> If you do not currently have a gym at your home, this option includes assistance with equipment selection and home-gym design. Your home personal-training program also includes a full nutritional analysis, help with grocery shopping, complete training-program design and phone and e-mail support.

After establishing a client base, I removed this option, and now charge a consulting fee of $150 per hour to visit a client's home and make recommendations for gym equipment and size. I also charge for any extra hours outside the face-to-face session that I may spend in phone conversation or e-mailing the client.

Home personal training is comfortable and easy. If desired, you can work from a home office, eliminate the studio and gym, and only train clients at home. If you live in a large metropolitan area with many wealthy individuals, this possibility can be very attractive.

Finally, in the same way that I offer my services to travel to a corporate site for a wellness presentation, I will travel to a home to present to a club or group. I charge a $250 seminar fee and speak for 45 minutes with a 15 minute Q&A. I have been hired primarily by women's groups, such as Moms in Motion and Weight Watcher's, to come to a home on a weekday evening and give such a presentation, which can be a nice addition to your home personal-training business. Just remember my "One Step Ahead" time-management strategy:

When designing a weekly or monthly seminar or class series, remember that you don't necessarily need a syllabus for the entire clinic. You simply need to stay "one step ahead" of your students or audience. I've often advertised and sold spaces for a clinic that didn't even exist until several days before it occurred. Nobody needs to know that the fantastic nutrition powerpoint that you announce that you'll be presenting next week has not yet been created. In the same way that it can be easy on the pocketbook to pay for a car as you go, it can save you large chunks of time to create your content as you go. Furthermore, why waste your time designing a syllabus if there doesn't turn out to be any interest in your content? In this manner, if there actually is lack of interest, you can cancel the clinic, or simply spend a minimal amount of time in material preparation. Focus on preparing high-quality content for the venues at which you anticipate having a large audience. Remember, your time is valuable.

Corporate Training

As the business world becomes more aware of the significant positive correlation between worker health and worker productivity, corporate wellness is catching on big. I allude to this fact in my sales letter and advertising to corporations. Figure 9-2 details a sample sales letter for a corporate-wellness program.

Obviously, to offer a program within the scope of the description listed in the letter detailed in Figure 9-2, you will find yourself a full-time corporate-personal trainer, which results in very good money. If you want to have the time to continue your other enterprises, then establish an LLC and hire trainers as employees to oversee the program for you, or simply subcontract to trainers using a 1099-MISC form.

The fee model and corporate-fitness program that I offer has various levels and packages. Figure 9-3 gives an example of a complete corporate-wellness package.

All of this information should be enough to get your creative juices flowing! The last package listed is a feature that I offer by working in close conjunction with my sports-medicine facility. Executive health is a great way to make money, because corporations will pay you top dollar to take care of their precious CEOs.

Whether home or corporate based, an off-site personal-training program is a perfect solution for a trainer who wants to enhance their income, or eliminate the hassle of a studio or gym. Like the digital-information product, the biggest advantage is that there are very few costs involved. Not having to pay a lease or maintain equipment leaves you with much less headache and more money in your pocket. Use the examples in this chapter to launch your off-site training business tomorrow!

Sample Corporate-Wellness Sales Letter

Pacific Elite Fitness offers innovative online employee-fitness programs and wellness strategies that allow employees to easily access their personal fitness coach from anywhere in the world.

In the initial phase of your complete wellness program, a certified exercise professional will visit your facility to conduct one-on-one interviews with enrolled employees, gathering pertinent exercise, health, and nutrition information to design a customized program for each employee, complete with ideal goals and a fitness/nutrition program for each employee. This individual is your corporate-personal trainer, and will be equipped with the knowledge and forms to conduct a synergistic interaction between the employee, the employee's physician, and your corporate-health insurance in order to design the proper individualized program.

After data is gathered, your corporate-personal trainer will design a customized exercise and nutrition program for each enrolled employee. Each individual will receive his program via e-mail, as well as access to exercise photo- and video-libraries and a free wellness-article database.

In addition, once a month, your corporate-personal trainer will visit your facility to present a wellness seminar on fitness, nutrition, and healthy-lifestyle choices, as well as conduct a group Q&A on the corporate-wellness fitness and nutrition plans. Your business will be on the cutting edge of corporate wellness, and your employees will have a job perk to rave about.

All these features are included at merely a fraction of the cost an employee would face if attempting to hire their own personal trainer or nutritionist, and require a minimal investment from the employer, with the option of an employee co-pay. Most importantly, the investment in health has been shown to offer great dividends, both physically and financially, which ultimately improves your company's bottom line.

In 1999, the U.S. medical bill was $738 million, of which businesses paid 30 percent. Current traditional approaches involve waiting until after a worker has become ill or injured, then paying for the necessary treatments. A much more proactive approach requires well-designed prevention and health promotion, which, as research has demonstrated, will lower your company's health-care expenditures and increase worker productivity. Several studies show impressive results through reduced medical-insurance premiums, lower turnover rates, less worker's compensation claims, fewer sick days, shorter hospital stays, and other direct health benefits of a physically-fit employee.

The incorporation of a personal, customized-fitness program for each employee also offers the advantage of increasing employee benefits by becoming a part of the total compensation package. This program offers a flexible method to compensate employees and has a positive effect on the company's bottom line. Whoever heard of adding perks and not only saving money, but actually getting a return on your investment? Multiple studies support the fact that a physically fit employee is happier, healthier, and more productive. Fit employees create a fit company, and with health costs and the costs of running a business rising, you now have a way to simultaneously cut expenses and create a happier employee.

Smart companies are equipped to make smart and innovative decisions. This decision can be a chance to set your company apart. To act now, contact Ben Greenfield at elite@pacificfit.net or call XXX-XXX-XXXX and your complete corporate wellness program can be fully operational within one month.

Figure 9-2

Sample Corporate-Wellness Program

- *Total Corporate-Wellness Package*. A complete wellness package, designed to decrease employee health-premium costs and improve workplace productivity and morale. The package includes the following:
  - ✓ One monthly wellness assessment for each employee. Health interviews and evaluations are performed by a corporate personal trainer at the worksite.
  - ✓ A complete individualized fitness and nutrition program design for each employee. Customized exercise and diet programs are delivered to your employees via e-mail. The program includes online support, exercise photos and videos, and a free wellness-article database.
  - ✓ One monthly 60-minute wellness workshop at your corporate site, which includes topics, such as stress management, wellness in the workplace, and travel exercise and nutrition.
  - ✓ Pricing. All prices include combined employer/employee contribution. Corporations are responsible for collecting employee contribution via salary deduction or pay-in program. Employer payments are then made to Pacific Elite Fitness via secure online direct debit (recommended) or monthly paper billing. Corporations are only billed for the actual number of employees enrolled in the program.

    <u>5-20 enrolled employees</u>
    $300 initial set-up fee
    $60 per employee per month (six-month contract)
    $55 per employee per month (one-year contract)

    <u>21-100 enrolled employees</u>
    $450 initial set-up fee
    $50 per employee per month (six-month contract)
    $45 per employee per month (one- year contract)

    <u>101+ enrolled employees</u>
    $600 initial set-up fee
    $40 per employee per month (six-month contract)
    $30 per employee per month (one-year contract)

- *Corporate Wellness-Seminar Series*: One 60-minute wellness seminar at your corporate site, including topics, such as stress management, wellness in the workplace, and travel and exercise nutrition. Recommended on a monthly basis. Price: $250 per seminar
- *Corporate Group Personal-Training Package*: For four weeks, a corporate group of 8 to 12 employees can work with a fitness and diet expert at the corporate site gym or health facility. The entire group meets with a personal trainer for a group exercise program once a week for one hour. Price: $2100

Figure 9-3

- *Corporate Individual Personal Training*: We offer innovative online employee-fitness programs and wellness strategies that allow employees to easily access their fitness program from anywhere in the world. It doesn't matter whether your gym is at a corporate facility, off-site club, home, or hotel room—all workouts are customized based on each employee's personal profile, fitness level, and exercise equipment access. Normally, individual personal training with Pacific Elite Fitness is $150 per session. However, any employee involved with a corporation currently signed up for any of the above packages receives an automatic 15 percent discount on individual personal training.
- *Corporate Consulting and Facility Design*: Whether you are renovating an existing facility or building a new fitness center, we provides certified-consulting services to assist you in creating a well-planned and dynamic facility that offers safety, performance, and aesthetic appeal. We will work closely with your design team to develop a facility that minimizes risk while offering potential for the highest possible facility utilization and employee satisfaction. Features include facility layout, equipment recommendations, budget planning, demographic analysis, and safety regulation. Price: based on bid. (Note: I usually determine how many hours I anticipate putting into the project, then bid at $150 per hour).
- *Executive Health Screening*: with our access to a full range of medical, physiologic, and biomechanics procedures, Pacific Elite Fitness can offer executives a safe and effective way to screen for potential exercise risks and to track fitness parameters. The staff of nutritionists, physiologists, physical therapists, and physicians at Champions Sports Medicine can provide a full spectrum of health information and advise an executive on the proper steps to minimize health risks and maximize effectiveness of an exercise or diet program. The executive health screening consists of the following procedures:
  - ✓ Medical examination and physical screening by a physician
  - ✓ Resting/exercise electrocardiogram and blood pressure
  - ✓ Complete blood count and comprehensive metabolic profile
  - ✓ Thyroid screening
  - ✓ Body composition testing
  - ✓ Nutritional consultation with a registered dietitian
  - ✓ Exercise and resting metabolic testing
  - ✓ Blood lactate testing
  - ✓ Gait analysis
  - ✓ Sweat-sodium analysis

This package is a gold-standard screening program right at your backdoor, and can easily be included with a corporate-wellness bid.

Price: varies depending on desired services.

Figure 9-3 (cont.)

10

Marketing Yourself

There's a reason that the best personal trainers in the world aren't necessarily the wealthiest. Marketing is a key component of the fitness business, and this chapter teaches you how to find your niche market, get published in newspapers and magazines, become a recognized television-fitness celebrity, maximize your expo-booth presence and saturate the community and country with your expertise! You'll learn how to optimize and format your press releases, how to be featured on your local television station whenever you please, and how to charge top dollar for your public appearances.

No matter how talented you are, you're not going to make any money unless you're discovered. Think about famous pop stars. Britney Spears is not necessarily the best musician on the planet; however, she has the marketing down. Through television appearances, niche marketing, press releases, newspaper and magazine articles, and highly public presence, she has established herself as a celebrity. Granted, she had a few lucky breaks along the way, like Disney, but the point of the example is that to make the big bucks, you don't have to be the best—you just have to be the most popular.

How are your clients discovering you? How are you establishing your celebrity presence as a personal trainer? Do you have a plan for taking over your local, and eventually national, fitness market? If not, keep reading.

Identify Your Niche

Some trainers have the mindset that they will first become a popular trainer, and then settle on the niche market that they most want to train, once they don't have to worry about the "bread-and-butter" clients. This approach is completely contradictory to the way you should be thinking.

If you establish your niche market, the other markets will take notice. I began as the well-known local triathlon coach who expanded into the rest of the market as my coached athletes realized that I also knew quite a bit about weight loss and nutrition. I used newspaper and magazine stories, as well as client testimonials, to drop hints that I did more than just coach triathletes. I'd use techniques, such as ending an interview with, "What many people don't realize is that many of the same key concepts that we teach for faster swimming, cycling, and running can be used for highly effective weight-loss and nutrition management." Suddenly my very specific niche market expanded into a broad clientele base. However, my high "niche market" pricing remained the same for the "non-niche" clients.

What is your niche market from which to begin your marketing campaign? The following scenarios can be used to whet your appetite:

- *Wedding weight loss for brides-to-be*. Advertise at bridal shows and wedding dress stores, and share your business contact information with wedding planners.
- *Vertical jump-maximizing techniques*. Advertise at local AAU basketball events, three-on-three basketball tournaments, sand volleyball events, and local high school track and field teams.
- *Quick fitness for busy CEOs*. Advertise at your corporate seminars (refer to Chapter 9), the airport, and yes, for this one, the gym.
- *Fitness for strippers*. Call them exotic dancers if you want. You know where to advertise. Word will spread. This ones my favorite, from which I've actually generated quite robust referral business.

Press Releases and Newspapers

Knowing how to write a properly-formulated press release is a must. I use press releases whenever I need to alert the local newspapers and magazines about:
- Books I've released (whether e-books or otherwise)
- Awards I've received
- Camps or clinics I'm running
- Public speaking events in which I'm appearing
- Any newspapers or magazines in which I've been published (yes, the local media will cover other media coverage)

I simply maintain an e-mail list of the editors for all the local newspapers and health or fitness publications, and whenever the opportunity arises, I'll send out a press release, using a simple press-release template. Figure 10-1 is a sample press release from a recently released announcement about a project for which I self-published and self-replicated a book and DVD.

It's very important to include detailed information like source, release date, media contacts and locations/dates. Having seen my sample press release, compare it to the template illustrated in Figure 10-2.

Amazingly, if your release is properly formatted, a large number of the media publications to which you send your release will likely publish part or all of your press release—and it's free. Another side benefit is that the newspaper or publication staff will grow familiar with your name and may contact you to contribute to their stories, rather than you having to push information their direction.

Sample Product Press Release

Ben Greenfield
0123 X STREET
000-000-0000
elite@pacificfit.net
www.pacificfit.net

*Release source: Ben Greenfield

FOR IMMEDIATE RELEASE:

Local Author Releases Comprehensive Nutrition and Exercise Guide

LIBERTY LAKE, WA – JUNE 6, 2005 – Ben Greenfield, a Spokane-based personal trainer and triathlete coach, has published an exercise and nutrition manual entitled *Shape21: The Complete 21-Day Lean-Body Manual*. Relying on over seven years of experience in assisting individuals of all fitness levels to boost the metabolism, burn fat, and gain lean muscle, Ben developed *Shape21* to be a simple guide that provides step-by-step instructions for quick and efficient weight loss.

Shape21 includes detailed plans for each day of a three-week program, providing exercise descriptions and photos, meal plans and recipes, and over 120 pages of healthy tips and tricks in a clear and easy-to-follow format. The manual also includes an exercise DVD, which shows a video of each exercise in the program.

Ben designed *Shape21* to adapt a broad range of levels, including beginner workouts for people who have never exercised, intermediate workouts for the average fitness level, and advanced workouts for athletes and very fit individuals. Each workout is designed to accomplish superior results with minimal equipment, usually requiring only the body weight or a small set of hand weights. The nutritional plan and recipes in Shape21 are based on a proper balance of fruits, vegetables, lean proteins, whole grains, and healthy fats.

"I wrote *Shape21* to be practical and convenient," said Ben Greenfield. "Being healthy and staying fit shouldn't involve exercising for three hours or carrying a calorie calculator to a restaurant. Staying lean and healthy should fit in as a normal, achievable part of your lifestyle, and not an inconvenience."

Shape21 is available at Ben's online personal-training website, Pacific Elite Fitness at www.pacificfit.net, as well as various gyms and bookstores in the Spokane and Coeur d' Alene area. Link to Publication*: http://www.shape21.com

About the Author
Ben Greenfield is certified by the National Strength and Conditioning Association as a Certified Personal Trainer and Strength and Conditioning Specialist. He graduated from University of Idaho with a bachelor's degree in Sports Science and a master's degree in Exercise Physiology.

About Pacific Elite Fitness
Founded in 2005, Pacific Elite Fitness is a web source for personal training, triathlete coaching, corporate-wellness programs, and free fitness and nutrition advice. Please visit www.pacificfit.net for more information.

Media contact: Ben Greenfield, elite@pacificfit.net, xxx-xxx-xxxx

Figure 10-1

Press Release Template

Contact person: _____

Company name: _____

Voice phone number: _____

FAX number: _____

E-mail address: _____

Website URL: _____

FOR IMMEDIATE RELEASE:

0123, Inc. Announces New Product Release

This headline is one of the most important components of the press release and needs to immediately grab the attention of the newspaper editor. The headline should be in bold type and a font that is larger than the body text. Preferred type fonts are arial, times new roman, or verdana. Keep headline to 80 to 125 characters maximum. Capitalize each word with the exception of "a," "the," "an," or any word that is three characters or less.

<City>, <State>, <Date> – Your first paragraph of the release should be written in a clear and concise manner. The opening sentence contains the most important information; keep it to 25 words or less. This section of your press release must also grab the reader's attention.

Answer the questions "who," "what," "when," "where," "why," and "how." Include crucial information about your product, service, or event, including where it can be purchased and, if possible, the cost. If you're writing about an event, include the date, location of the event, and any other pertinent information. Try to include a quote from someone that is a credible source of information (it can be yourself), list the title or position with the company, and why the person is considered a credible source. Don't be afraid to talk about yourself in the third person. You can include information on any awards the person has won, and published articles or public appearances.

Keep all sentences and paragraphs short; a paragraph should be no more than three to four sentences. The actual press release should be between 500 and 800 words, typed, professionally proofread, and spell-checked for errors. The press release does not use a sales pitch. Simply tell the facts and let the reader act upon those facts.

In the last paragraph before the company information, give instructions for additional information on the product or press-release subject, including a contact name or a call to action, such as "visit www.yoururl.com." Include details on product availability and any available samples or demos in this section.

ABOUT <COMPANY> – Include a brief description of your company along with the products and services it provides.

END – At the end of the release, you need to indicate to the journalists that the release is ended. Just type "End" on the first line after your text is completed.

Figure 10-2

Magazines

Fitness, health, and nutrition magazines, whether local, regional, or national, are another great way to establish yourself as an expert and increase your visibility. Once again, similar to press releases for newspapers, you must jump through certain literary hoops to satisfy the requirements of picky magazine editors. The nice part is that, unlike newspapers, the magazines will actually pay you anywhere from $75 to $600 for your stories and insight.

Figure 10-3 is a sample-query letter to a magazine for an article I wrote several years ago. Similar to press releases, you must include certain elements in your query. The Internet is a great place to find magazine-query templates. This query is for a nationally syndicated men's health and fitness magazine.

Sample Magazine-Query Letter

Dear editor:

Triathletes are intimidating. They're the group with the sculpted thighs, streamlined torso, and ripped shoulders. Yet despite their strapping proportions, they can somehow make you feel like you're standing still on the treadmill. Unfortunately, not everyone has the time, motivation, or gear to train with the frequency and volume required to actually complete a triathlon.

I'd like to offer your magazine a 1500-word article titled "Train Like a Triathlete." The article would discuss how the average gym populace can engage in an intense, metabolism-boosting weekly routine that simulates the demand and intensity of triathlon training, but doesn't require registering for a race, purchasing a $4000 bike, or even shaving your legs. This article would include information on how to:

- Stack functional resistance-training techniques with cardio "surges" to simulate the full-body intensity of triathlon training
- Incorporate cable and core exercises that build Phelps-esque lats, shoulders, and midsection, without having to squeeze into a Speedo®
- Simultaneously gain enormous lung capacity and aggressive muscular power, while still retaining lean muscle mass
- Achieve optimal heart-rate intensities and muscle utilization for peak calorie burning during cardiovascular and resistance training

With a simple nudge in the right direction, I've found that individuals who engage in such a training program often quickly discover that they have the physical ability to complete a triathlon (or at least the motivation to click the "register" button on a triathlon's web page).

I hope this topic interests you, and look forward to your response. If you would like to see the article, I can have it on your desk within two weeks of receiving your go-ahead. I can also provide you with complementary copies of all my books on health and fitness. Thank you for your time.

To your health,
Ben Greenfield

Figure 10-3

Always include an eye-catching opener, a brief overview of your story, the anticipated story audience, and a plan of action for the editor. Be as specific as possible.

The website of any major health and fitness publication will almost always include detailed contact information and query-submission requirements. Some sites only allow e-mail queries, but others want to receive queries via postal mail with SASEs (self-addressed stamped envelopes).

Follow the rules, and you'll get published. If you can't find the rules posted on the magazine's website, call the posted number in the magazine or on the website and ask for the editor or his/her voicemail. Leave a detailed message, such as:

> "Hi, this is Ben Greenfield calling from Spokane, Washington. I have an exciting and unique story about how people can enhance their fitness by training like a triathlete, without actually having to do a triathlon. I need to know what I need to do to get this article into your hands. Please give me a call at xxx-xxx-xxxx or shoot me an e-mail at elite@pacificfit.net with your submission requirements. Again, that's xxx-xxx-xxxx or elite@pacificfit.net. I'm really excited to get this article to you. Thanks."

I no longer rely on such letters of query or phone calls to magazines, as they now contact me for stories (a side benefit of attaining expert status in your niche area). Once again, this illustration is a perfect example that if you do some of the necessary footwork in the beginning, you'll find yourself on cruise control after a couple years in this business.

Expos

Although the booths, displays, and content at fitness expos are usually fantastic, the actual sales and marketing skills can tend to be sadly subpar. Unless an attendee actually stops at a vendor's booth and specifically asks a question, they are often allowed to pass by undisturbed. The last time I attended a fitness expo, I literally cruised the entire room in five minutes flat.

On the other hand, I have also attended several investment expos, which feature a gathering of completely different folk, devoted to finance, marketing, business, capitalism, and economy. It takes me nearly 30 minutes to traverse just a single aisle of such events. With each step, I am greeted on either side by vendors eager to show me the benefit of their product. They literally step in front of me, make eye contact, and ask a simple question, such as "Where are you from?" or "What do you do?" Notice that these are open-ended questions and they take advantage of the fact that most people like to talk about themselves.

An important lesson can be learned from this comparison. If you represent your personal-training studio, nutrition business, or gym at a health and fitness expo, try to follow these three simple rules:

- *Don't sit behind your table*. Stand in front of it, and interrupt the flow of traffic that passes by your booth. Hold your information, brochures, or business cards in your left hand, and keep your right hand free to shake hands.

- *Make eye contact*. One of the best ways to traverse quickly through an expo is to avoid eye contact with each of the vendors. People will try to avoid you. As a vendor, find a way to catch their attention. Ask questions, smile, and find the eyes.

- *Be vocal*. Nobody will stop if you stand in front of your table and merely look them in the eyes. You must have audible content. Do not choose common phrases like "How's it going," "Hi," or "Would you like a free sample?" These are close-ended statements. Instead, try something like, "Where did you get that shirt/blouse/tie?" or "So, what brings you to the expo today?" or "What kind of work do you do?"

Don't feel bad about interrupting a person's path. They came to the expo, and are probably expecting to be approached. You put in the hard work to have a booth and be a vendor, so make it count.

Three Top PR Tips

Sometimes, getting noticed by media, potential employers, and customers or clients feels like bashing your head against a brick wall. Throughout my years of experience in the fitness industry, I've found three highly-effective techniques to grab the attention of otherwise difficult-to-reach individuals: the squeaky wheel, the good ol' boys method, and the three-list method.

- The squeaky-wheel method. My mother always told me that "the squeaky wheel gets the oil, " which is another way of saying that persistence pays. Don't feel bad about repeatedly e-mailing, calling, or visiting your local television-news station, newspaper editor, or potential corporate-wellness client. The worst that can happen is you will eventually be told to go away. But in most scenarios, the target of your constant squeaking will realize that you may actually have something important to say. I visited my first corporate client HR director six times before he finally agreed to allow me to feature a monthly-wellness seminar to his employees.

- *The good-ol'-boys method.* It's all about who you know, and nowhere is this fact truer than the fitness industry, which closely resembles the sports-coaching network. Often, a football, basketball, or baseball coach lands a dream job because of ex-teammates, affiliations, or friends. The fitness industry is very similar. Do you want to write for a popular trade magazine? Are you constantly turned away by the editors? It may be more effective to call your personal-trainer friend across the country who has been published a half-dozen times and ask them to put in a good word for you. My wellness instructor from college landed me my first piece in a major men's fitness publication, simply because she had written an article for them in the past.

- *The three-list method.* Public relations require solid writing skills. The three-list method is one of the most effective techniques that I use when selling a product or selling myself. Simply think of three strong attributes that your product represents, and name them. Use no less and no more than three attributes. For example, you are experienced, well-educated, and have a dynamic personality. Your new fitness book is practical, easy-to-understand, and can be immediately utilized. The three tips you've just learned will allow you to turn heads, land high-paying fitness gigs, and sell products effectively.

Public Speaking

While the corporate-seminar presentations and home or club seminars discussed in Chapter 9 are one form of public speaking, another highly profitable form of public speaking is television appearances. To make yourself stand out in your local community, and eventually move on to even broader recognition, you need to find a way to get yourself in front of as many people as possible, and your local TV news station offers a perfect platform. The following strategy could be used:

- Every day, scan the local newspaper for fitness or diet articles that are relevant to your expertise. Watching your local news can also be beneficial, but only if you're practicing effective time-management techniques, like exercising during the news hour.

- Once relevant information is made public, it's time for you to make your move. For example, let's say a newspaper-article headline reads, "Exercise Linked to Decreased Diabetes Mortality." Call your local television stations via the news-reporting number that is readily available in the phonebook or station website and present the following statement to them:

  "Hi, this is _____(your name). I'm a local fitness professional, and noticed the recent newspaper headline about the association between exercise and decreased death from diabetes. I'm curious if your station had considered pursuing a story on how exercise is affecting individuals with diabetes. I have several individuals that I work with on a daily basis who are struggling with diabetes, which would be a really fantastic human-interest piece." (Yes, they love the human-interest piece line).

- Proceed to clearly and succinctly provide the station with your contact information. Prior to calling the station, contact any clients who would be a part of the story, and receive their permission to give the station their contact information, and to appear in a filmed workout for the television story.

Two things could happen now: one, the station either decides to pursue the story, or two, they decide not to. I've found that the television industry has a great memory. If they don't cover this story, and a story ever does arise for which they need expert fitness advice, and they have your contact information, they'll contact you.

Of course, you may get lucky and encounter a client who happens to be a television executive. This situation happened to me, and after two months of training, I received a random phone call from her news station. They wanted to do a story on science-based exercise, and they wanted to film me training a client and explaining the science of exercise physiology. Sometimes you just luck out.

An interesting phenomenon is that whenever I have a television appearance, which happens about once a month, I notice that my online-newsletter sign-up frequency goes through the ceiling for one or two days following the story. If I didn't have an online presence and the list generating tools discussed in Chapter 4, I wouldn't be reaping the benefits of enhanced clientele-contact information from television appearances. In this case, I know that the majority of the people that sign up are going to be local clients interested in personal training, so I can e-mail those people directly.

Imagine seeing a "fitness celebrity" on TV, signing up for his online newsletter, and then receiving a personalized e-mail from the same celebrity the next day, offering you a special one-year membership deal on personal training. Your waitlist of clients can be as long as you desire, and you can then begin charging top dollar. Accordingly, be prepared for the flow of interest when you get your 15 minutes of fame.

Many good personal trainers exist out there, but very few who actually maximize their leverage with the marketing tools presented in this chapter. Thus, they're stuck struggling with stale and traditional marketing techniques like hanging a poster on the gym wall that says "buy 10 sessions, get one free." Don't be that personal trainer, because the salary ceiling tops out very quickly. Instead, you need to build a waiting list for your services that allows you to charge whichever price that you choose and to train a minimum number of high paying, highly-motivated clientele. Pair this factor with time management, outsourcing busy work, information-product sales, high-yielding corporate and home-training strategies, an online-consulting business, supplement and nutrition income, physician networking, and public speaking and you have the ultimate platform to *train for top dollar*.

About the Author

Ben Greenfield is recognized as one of the top fitness, triathlon, nutrition, and metabolism experts in the nation. In 2008, he was voted as the Personal Trainer of the Year by the National Strength and Conditioning Association, an internationally recognized and respected certifying agency. Ben is president of Human Wellness Solutions, a network of facilities in the Inland Northwest that provides fat loss, nutrition, and human performance services. Ben is director of sports performance and oversees the physiology and biomechanics laboratory at Champions Sports Medicine in Spokane, WA, which offers metabolic-based weight loss, bicycle fitting, running gait analysis, swim stroke analysis, VO_{2max} testing, blood lactate testing, resting metabolic-rate analysis, and other cutting-edge procedures for weight loss and performance.

In college, Ben competed in tennis, water polo, and volleyball, and now competes as the number one-ranked triathlete for Triathlon Northwest. As an author of multiple books on fitness, metabolism, and diet, Ben specializes in nutrition, weight loss, triathlete analysis, coaching, and endurance athlete-program design. His credentials include:

- Bachelor's and master's degrees from University of Idaho in sports science and exercise physiology
- Personal training and strength and conditioning certifications from the National Strength and Conditioning Association (NSCA)
- Sports nutrition certification from the International Society of Sports Nutrition (ISSN)
- Advanced bicycle-fitting certification from Serotta International Cycling Institute
- Over nine years experience in coaching professional, collegiate, and recreational athletes from all sports

Ben hosts the highly popular fitness, nutrition, and wellness website at www.bengreenfieldfitness.com, which features his blogs, podcasts, and product reviews. He is a frequent contributor to the outdoor sports magazine *OutThere Monthly* and has been featured in magazines including *Inlander*, *In-Health*, *Triathlete*, and *Inside Triathlon*. As a public speaker on fitness, nutrition, and training, Ben has been the keynote lecturer at the Hawaii Ironman Triathlon Medical Conference, the Coeur D' Alene Ironman Medical Conference, Fleet Feet Sports Endurance Sports Clinic, and REI Nutrition Clinic. Ben is the owner of Pacific Elite Fitness, an online multi-sport coaching and training service, and also sits on the board of directors for Tri-Fusion triathlon team, Mt. Capra Nutrition, and the Fellowship of Christian Athletes.

In addition to coaching and training for weight loss and sports performance, Ben serves as a business and marketing consultant to fitness professionals, works as a web design and sales copywriter for Internet marketers, and is the owner of the website trainfortopdollar.com. For more information on enhancing your income as a personal trainer, nutritional consultant, or gym owner, or to sign-up for Ben's free business blog and podcast, visit the *Train For Top Dollar* website. You may also find Ben's fitness business articles at PTontheNet.com, PersonalTrainerToday.com, and *FitPro* magazine.

> Stay tuned to www.trainfortopdollar.com, where Ben Greenfield features free weekly columns on new, highly-effective strategies to maximize your income as a personal trainer. Be sure to sign up for the free newsletter, and subscribe to the blog and podcast. Simply visit www.trainfortopdollar.com and click on "blog." E-mail your questions to support@trainfortopdollar.com.